I'M NOT AFRAID TO DIE

I'M NOT AFRAID TO DIE

by

AN IRISH HOUSEWIFE

THE MERCIER PRESS
DUBLIN and CORK

THE MERCIER PRESS, 4 Bridge Street, Cork
25 Lower Abbey Street, Dublin 1.

ISBN O 85342 434 9

To My Husband

Printed by Cahill & Co. Limited, East Wall Road, Dublin 3

CHAPTER

1

The early spring sunshine flooded the doctor's waiting-room. Like a homing pigeon I headed for the chinz covered couch with the broken spring. I smiled at the two other patients, obviously two mothers-to-be. They smiled back at me before resuming their conversation. Pre-natal exercises, relaxation classes, breast-feeding, nappies — their lively voices droned on and on.

The sun shone on the faded patch on the wall where a picture had been removed. I idly wondered what they had done with the picture. The loud shouts of children playing rose from the large back garden. The doctor had five sons and they were obviously in the middle of a game of cops and robbers. The wild cries of 'Lie down, Charlie — lie down you, are shot!' echoed into the room every so many minutes. Charlie it seemed had not a notion of lying down, shot or otherwise.

I scanned aimlessly through a magazine — How many times had I sat in this corner in the past, I mused. How many times had I persuaded myself that this was my last visit. I had come with anaemia, gastric 'flu, ordinary 'flu and what have you. Each time I had convinced myself that I was knocking at Death's Door. Each time I recovered of course. Then twice I had been given the wonderful news that I was pregnant. That added two more patients to be brought — tonsils, colds, measles, mumps, jaundice — you name it they got it and sometimes with a relapse for good measure.

The door bell rang and an old lady was shown in. She sat down and obviously felt very nervous. She picked up a magazine and pretended to read. There was a slight tremour in her wrinkled, freckled hands.

George, the doctor, and I were friends since childhood. We had grown up in the same suburb. He was three or four years older than I and used carry me to school on the bar of his bike when I was very young. He was always interested in medicine and joined the Red Cross in his early teens. If a model was needed for him to practise his prowess at bandaging, I was called on to render my services. A session with George in those days was a rather traumatic experience. He was quite liable to get very mixed up and one was in danger of having ones arm or shoulder blades actually broken by faulty First Aid. He took me to a First Aid Display one day as his model or victim. He won First Prize and was very proud of himself. I remember he bought me ice-cream and lemonade on the way home and my arms ached from the slings and splints I had had to suffer for his sake.

George went to University. He used come home for holidays and mid-term breaks. He often called and told me about his progress, the hard work, the non-stop examinations and non-stop romances.

Meanwhile, back at the ranch, so to speak, I finished school and I went to Commercial College and graduated into an office job. George also graduated, much to the relief of his long suffering mother. He fell madly in love, for the last time. They got married. He started a slow but sure practise.

I too fell in love — just once — and got married. I became the mother of a boy and a girl. How I enjoyed my pram pushing days. There they were laid out like altars with frills and lace. I marched with my pram up and down the town to show off my two beautiful children. Every mother thinks she has the most outstanding children in the world. I was definitely no exception to the rule.

As I day-dreamed I moved on the couch as the pain in my back rose to engulf me. A lump had appeared on my back, for no apparent reason, last summer. Naturally, I headed straight down to George. That visit was followed by tests, injections, X-rays and more tests, more injections and more X-rays.

Then pain became my constant companion. To wake up in the morning without the pain was like a hundred pounds to me. As the day wore on I'd know it would be back before nightfall. Painkillers were really not strong enough.

The dawn often broke and I would like awake

watching the sky change colour. The whole house would be asleep. Many is the sunrise I'd seen with six o'clock feeds. I'd recall those hectic days. Falling out of bed at the first hungry roar. Heating bottles, feeding and changing. The nicest part of motherhood in those days was the moment the baby would go back to sleep and I would fall back into bed again.

'Next, Madam,' the receptionist broke in on my thoughts. I looked around me to discover that the two mothers-to-be were gone and all that was left was me and the old lady. She was busy doing a bit of knitting and nodded as I went out.

I went into the surgery.

'Hello, George,' I said brightly.

He had his back turned to me and was studying my X-rays. His hair curled over his collar. There was a crease in the back of his jacket. George was always easy going about his appearance, even as a boy.

'It's a lovely day, George,' I said, trying in vain to get him to turn around and face me. 'Are they my X-rays down from Dublin?' I asked.

George turned around. He tossed the X-rays onto a side table. He spread his hands out on his desk and towered over me.

'Ellen,' he began.

His voice was not the usual professional doctor-cum-friend. It was a bity shaky. Like the time, long ago when he told me our dog had been run over by a car.

'Ellen,' he began again, 'the news is not so good this time'.

'I know,' I whispered.

'Of course,' he continued, 'they are trying out new drugs all the time, but an operation would be out of the question even now.'

'I know, George,' I said firmly.

'I thought they had made a mistake,' he continued, as if I had never spoken. 'I sent the X-rays to Cork as well for a double check and the two specialists agree.'

He looked me straight in the face. His expression was exactly the same as it had been when he was about seventeen. He came up to tell me that his current girlfriend, Jane, had thrown him over. I covered his hand with mine.

'Do you understand me, George,' I asked quietly, 'I know it is bad news this time — I have been waiting for it'.
'How,' he asked more to himself than to me, 'how do people with Cancer always know?'
'I think I have known from the beginning, George,' I said; 'it is definitely hopeless isn't it?'
He just looked at me silently.
'How long George — tell me the truth — how long have I got?' I asked quietly.
George gathered his composure and took up the X-rays again.
'It is impossible to tell,' he said, 'but the growth is still small. You could have eighteen months to two years at the very outside.'
'George,' I continued, 'how long out of that time have I for being an active wife and mother. How long more have I for laughing, dancing, playing, walking, cycling — how long?'
'Lets say until next spring, Ellen,' he whispered hoarsly, 'I cannot promise any more than that.'
We sat and looked at each other. We had both known the truth a long time but were each afraid to face it. The X-rays had at last proved that we were both right.
'Will you tell Francis tonight,' he questioned, 'or would you like me to call out and tell him.'
'No,' I shouted, 'we will tell him next spring.'
'But,' he argued, 'he is your husband, he has a right to know.'
'He will know soon enough,' I replied.
'How are you going to keep it from him?' he asked.
'I shall be busy doing a few things I have always intended to do,' I replied.
'Things?' he repeated, 'what things.'
'First,' I said quite seriously, 'first I am going to write a book.'
'A book?' he repeated after me, 'now?'
'Yes, George, now,' I said.
He walked as far as the front door with me. We shook hands.

'I'll see you next month as usual George?' I questioned him. He nodded.

I walked down the steps and looked back at him. He stood tall and thin and very bewildered looking.

'A book,' he called after me, 'a book. . . that is the end.'

'Yes,' I thought to myself, 'this is the end.'

CHAPTER

2

On the way home from George's surgery, I stopped. I sat on a seat by the river. The chestnut tree's sticky leaf buds shone in the sunshine. The river glistened and the cars and vans buzzed around the streets of the town like coloured ants on a fancy ant hill. An anonymous river flowing beside an anonymous town. A fist of anonymous shops and a few thousand anonymous people. And me. I looked closer at the town. There is the place where my husband works. There is the children's school, there is where my mother lives. There is our home. This is not an anonymous town — it is my home town. I have set my roots here and one day I will be laid to rest in the new cemetery. My family will live on in this town. If they leave and settle somewhere else, it will leave a mark on them. Part of their hearts will belong to this place of their birth.

This is the town in which I have dreamed dreams. This is the town in which I have had some of my dreams come true. All my life I have had dreams—they turned to ambitions and in turn became obsessions. Writing a book has been one of them. Actually I had fancied writing a a marathon like *War and Peace*. George has given me a fabulous excuse — I have not the time really! How can I joke under the circumstances? Well, Death and I have met before — we have fought and I have won. This time my chances do not look so good, but I refuse to curl up in a corner and cringe.

With those fighting words I intend to really start! I am armed with a 4p biro and a 9p copy-book, the first of many I hope. If the reader has any picture of me on a deserted island banish the thought at once. I am in the midst of running a home. Many is the stew that will be eaten in the next few weeks. Many is the lick and promise that will be given to my lovely semi-detached. I pray to God to keep the grass and weeds at bay while I tell my story.

The first whisper of my existence became known on my mother's forty-eight birthday. She had been feeling poorly for some time. She had put her fatigue and heartburn down to the change of life. Her family was reared, the youngest being ten. She was looking forward practically to grandchildren at that stage. However, God spoke first, as they say. She sauntered into her G.P. for a check-up and tore home with the news that she was seven months pregnant. My four sisters were delighted and my father was overjoyed at the thoughts of a son at long last.

She has a favourite chair in the front room and she sits in that whenever she gets a shock or a surprise. Always, if you have news for her, she first makes for the chair and then lets you deliver your message. My sisters maintain that having told them the good tidings she sat in that chair for a full month from sheer shock! I was due to arrive for Christmas. On top of a queasy stomach, a burning heart, a turkey, presents and the rest of Christmas a baby was all my mother needed to add to the excitement. Herself and my sisters knitted away like demons, everything in blue of course. My father whistled and sang and thought up all the great games he could at last play with a boy.

On 22 November, never mind the year, my mother was washing up the ware after the dinner. Her sister, luckily enough, was there helping her. My aunt tells it that my mother gave a run out the hall to go up to bed for her little daily after dinner nap. Next thing the aunt heard a roar from the hall —

'I've had him!' This news my mother screamed at the top of her lungs.

'Who?' shouted my aunt, who was not the most excitable in the world.

'The baby.'

That shifted the aunt. After that there was skin and hair flying. My aunt takes all the credit for bringing me into the world safely. She fixed the two of us up on the sofa and sent for my father. He arrived full of glee. My dad stood in awe as he surveyed me. I was very small, I was two and a half pounds and I was a girl. My aunt is a great one

11

for describing a scene. She has described the scene so often to me that I can see it as if I were a bystander. Her verbatum edition of it is 'There he stood, his dreams crashing around him. "Another daughter" was written all over his face. I felt it my duty to intervene.' (This particular aunt feels it her duty, on all occasions, to intervene!)

'Listen here,' says I (this is my aunt speaking), a boy at this stage would kill her (pointing at my mother) and she facing the Change and all – have sense now. Girls are quiet, easy to rear; look at the others, not a bit of bother!'

I spent the first two months of my life in a boot box. My mother wrapped me in cotton wool, placed me in the boot box and put it and me on top of the black stove in the kitchen. She fed me drops of milk laced with brandy from a fountain pen filler. She is worse than her sister for telling stories so I know that chapter of my life by heart. She does not spare on the drama when she tells it either. Seemingly Death hovered over that black stove day in, day out. I cried non-stop practically as if I sensed his presence. When I stopped crying she would look in the box to check if I were dead. She maintains that every time she looked in at me I was looking out at her. Seemingly I had huge eyes; I still have them, but now I have a bigger face. Anyway, the fear of finding me dead had her nerves at her. When she used see the pair of big eyes looking out at her, I used frighten the sugar out of her. The misfortunate woman and she doing her best.

One day during the boot box era, an old neighbour called. During the course of the conversation and cup of tea, I started to cry. My mother ignored me. Seemingly the old lady didn't. She pricked her ears and saw the boot box. 'God,' she commented to my mother, 'you should throw out that old cat up there. There is something wrong with the bloody thing.'

My mother stood up and threw out her chest.

'That,' she said, pointing at the boot box like Sarsfield pointing into Limerick, 'that is my baby daughter.'

The old lady thought she was joking. My mother permitted her a peep into the box. The two big eyes were staring out at her as usual out of the bed of cotton wool. Our guest nearly got a stroke laughing. To the day that old lady died, my mother never quite forgave her for her derision!

I eventually graduated out of the boot box. My mother had the full joys of motherhood in what she maintains were her twilight years. I ask you? I kept her amused by putting beads up my nose and devouring vast quantities of horse-hair stuffing out of my pram. She maintains that I never learned to crawl or walk. I just got up one day and started to run. I was always very small and being so near the ground I had perfect balance. She, of course, had to run after me. I kept her so fully occupied for the first few years of my life that she went in one side of the Change of Life and out the other without realising it.

I turned out to be the complete opposite to the dolly type little girl she had visions of. I had not much time for dolls but I had a Teddy Bear whom I really loved. Any gentle, maternal, womanly streaks I had, he brought them out in me. Of course, there were times when I used practically crucify him; it was all according to the mood I was in. I was a non-stop joy to my father. At last he had someone to play football with. I could shin up a tree fast as a wink. I used hang out the bedroom windows, get lost regularly in town and definitely make life a little more exciting for the two of them. My friends consisted of one little girl—and dozens of the neighbouring boys.

I can see our back garden with all those children in it. How my mother put up with the noise I'll never know. Windows being broken were a weekly occurance. The glazier practically took up residence with us for a few years. My mother used eat us, of course. My father used just smile and put another match to his ever outting pipe. Those days were lovely. Seems like the sun always shone and they were filled with laughter and playing. In the background Count John McCormack sang non stop. The lady next door was an ardent fan and her gramaphone ground out 'She is Far from the Land' & Co., day in, day out. She would often put her head out the window and shout, 'Do you hear him?' 'Oh, God isn't he marvellous.'

The glazier was there one day when she gave her usual comments.

'Jasus,' he shouted, 'you'd want to be deaf not to hear him, what is wrong with you?'

She looked at him agast.

'You can't beat Gigli,' he shouted, 'that fellow is useless.' She banged her window with such temper she broke it. She sent twenty miles for a glazier to put it in. We heard her telling him about the rowdy my mother had putting in her glass.

I loved those rough and tumble years. I was never without a torn knee or a black eye, sometimes both.

When I was about four years old, my grandmother used take me for a few months at a time to give my mother a break.

She was living sixty miles away in a lovely little town in the south. On my visits there, I never wore shoes. I was sent off each vacation with a new pair of tackys — you know, tennis shoes — and on the last day of my visit I'd walk along the water in them to give them a worn look. I also was allowed wear shorts. Mammy never warmed to the idea that they were ladylike and a lady she was determined to make of me. My grandmother had her own ideas on rearing me so I had the best of two worlds really.

My grandmother had a three bedroom terrace house the same as our own, and it was home from home for me all my life. When my grandmother had visitors, these were many and often, she used farm me out to an old friend of hers by the name of Tits Murphy. Tits got her pet name on account of having the hugest bosoms you ever laid eyes on. Beside her, Liz Taylor or Sofia Loren would look like ironing boards.

The first day I was farmed out to her I got a few shocks. First thing to strike me was that her house was in a graveyard. She seemingly took over the job of caretaker when her third husband died. The house originally was outside the gates of the graveyard but the graves kept creeping out around it, she explained. That was all right until it was time to go to the toilet. Sacred Heart of Almighty God, wasn't the tigin away over past, as she said, 'The Doggie Sullivans and the Fish Brennan's.' The Doggie Sullivan's had great greyhounds in their day and the other gang had a fine fish shop. When I had gone to the toilet from fright alone — she brought me on a tour of the 'beds'. She never once referred to them as graves. She showed me where all my ancestors slept and hers too into the bargain. She had her first husband buried at the north end of the graveyard. Her only comment was 'Michael O'Hara is there — black bastard from Skibbereen!'

Her third husband was at the southern end; he got a fantastic oration altogether.

'Poor old Spud,' she shouted at the clodded earth, 'the kindest bastard to ever breathe. I got him put here so that he would see the lights of the pubs and hear the laughing from the little bit of a knock shop he used visit. That was before he met me of course, I'll have you know. Never looked at another woman since he met me. Had to put pennies on his eyes and he nearly cold — couldn't take his eyes off me he couldn't.'

After the first few visits to Tits, I got used to her ways and it became yet another home from home. Living at home all the spring, winter and autumn, I had a rather strict upbringing. There was an abundance of love and affection but there were rules to be kept to. There were strict meal times and bed time. One had to be careful of ones clothes and behave so as not to disgrace the rest of them. Come summer I was packed off to Grandma's. There meal times were elastic, bed times were elastic and clocks meant nothing. One could ramble with the dogs along the dusty roads for hours. It would never dawn on anyone that I was lost. If I did get lost the dogs would turn for home soon enough. I used spend hours swinging on farmers' gates watching them all bustling about their business. I used help with the haymaking or just browse about alone or with my friends and cousins.

The times I'd be staying with Tits were an education in themselves. She had the most unique slant on Life, Death and the Hereafter I had ever come across. I think she has had the most influence on me as far as religion and living is concerned.

I remember one night I got tied up in knots saying the Rosary before going to sleep. I remember crying to to myself and Tits arrived in, in her white floor length cotton nightie. With the candle light flickering around her she was the image of an inflated apparition of Our Lady. Her waist length hair floating around her and all.

'What the hell is wrong with you?' she roared most un-Our Ladylike.

'I got tied up in the Rosary,' I wailed; 'I was fine the first trip around but I've got mixed up now.'

'You are on your second trip round those beads?' she asked in awe.

'Yes' I replied and to add conviction, 'Mother Brenda told us to say two Rosaries for a happy death.'

Tits got into a terrible fit of laughing.

'Well, I never,' she said, 'what will they think of next.'

'Do you not say the Rosary going to sleep, Tits?' I asked.

'Never,' she shouted, 'where would I get the time?' She parked herself on the side of the bed and I knew I was in for a lesson on living her way.

'When I go to bed,' said Tits, 'I say to God, "Jesus, your servant is jaded." That is my night prayers.'

'But,' I interupted.

'No "buts,"' she said, 'in the morning I say "Thank you Jesus for giving me another day." He knows then that everything I do in the day I do for him and with his help. What the hell would I be boring him with strings of prayers for? You do the same now. Those long rigmarolls are for nuns and priests who have damn all else to do.'

'But Mother Brenda — what about her?' I asked.

'What about her?' asked Tits loosing her patience and gathering her skirts around her. 'Let Mother Brenda and all the rest of them say the Rosary twice for themselves and four times for the two of us put together — bloody all else to do, the poor creatures.'

With that she left me.

I looked at my lovely little white beads and as if she read my thoughts in she floated again.

'Hold onto the beads, love,' she said softly, 'they are grand for saying at Mass or at a funeral. It looks well and you have the time during those cermonies. God hates time being wasted; sure my whole bloody life is a prayer and so is yours.'

With a swing of her bosoms she disappeared into the night and I felt closer to God than I ever did and I rolling off long complicated prayers.

For the first time and not the last I joined my hands and said, 'Jesus, your servant is jaded.'

While I was on my summer vacations my family used call to visit me and we would always spend an afternoon in Cork. The highlight of this was always having tea in Thompsons and taking home boxes of their cakes.

On one such expedition we met an old school chum of my mother's.

'Susan,' your one shouted at my mother, 'how are you at all and is this your family.'

She looked at my teenage sisters with admiration as they passed by with my Father.

Then she took one pennyworth of me.

'God, Susan,' says she, 'is this the baby, the scrapping of the skillet so to speak?'

The lowness my mother ignored.

'This,' said she and she holding me at arm's length, 'this is Ellen. Isn't she beautiful?'

'God,' says your one, 'She is a terrible weed altogether!'

How my mother refrained from beating the one up in Patrick Street is a first class miracle. All the way back to my grandmother's we had to listen to the creed, breed and generation of herself and all belong to her.

Shortly after that my mother tried to fatten me. Every tonic on the market was tried, but in vain. I remained like something after doing about five years in Belsen Consentration Camp.

Most of the pills I disposed of and she found them when the old sofa fell assunder years later.

CHAPTER

3

Each morning as I wave the children off to school, I feel a sense of relief. I have put them on the road for yet another day of their lives. I cannot understand other mothers being glad of being rid of their children during school hours. Every moment I have spent with my children has being a precious moment. If they called me to join a game, tools were downed immediately and off I would go, and still do. Walks and family outings have been the highlights of our lives. Will this togetherness help form their characters for the future? I do not know. I will not be there to see. Children's minds are very deep. Impressions leave lasting marks on them. I know, because I too was a child.

At the age of five I went to school. I left at sixteen. In the years in between the nuns did all in their power, as well as educate me, to break my spirit and break my heart.

First it was discovered I was not as bright as my sisters. For this they kept on and on at me. Then it was discovered I was left-handed.

Daily our writing nun smashed my knuckles with a ruler until I eventually got the message and wrote with my right hand. This she accomplished by nearly hitting my left hand until it was useless. I also acquired a slight faulter in my speech from pure nerves. This impediment was thought to be hilarious by our English nun. When I would be asked to say a poem, naturally, I would faulter. She would then have the whole class copy my manner of speech. This was mental cruelty of the highest order. It never dawned on me to tell them at home.

School to me was a completely different part of my life. Where at home I was treated with love and respect, I thought that this treatment doled out at school was natural, for a school.

Coming up to our First Holy Communion, Rev Mother used to threaten us unmercifully. If we told a lie after Confession, she told us, the Holy Communion would jump out of our mouths around the floor. If our fathers did not buy a black baby for half-a-crown, we would not be let next or near the altar.

The First Confession was a nightmare of months of preparation.

Mother Brenda told us what to say and how to say it. 'Bless me, Father, for I have sinned and this is my First Confession. I told two lies and I stole sweets at home.' That was the sins for the full class of us.

I, for one, had different ideas. I was supposed to have reached the age of reason and I so looked forward to a chat with the priest. I never told lies, no matter what the consequences, and I was given my quota of sweets. I just couldn't understand your one's attitude at all.

I was mid-way in the line for the Confessions and dreaming as usual. Mother Brenda gave me a knuckle in the head to wake me up and I reeled into the box. This was supposed to be a happy and holy occasion. Well, I was fit to kill her. 'Bless me, Father,' I began, taking a good look at him. The misfortunate priest was sitting with his head in his hands, practically in a semi-coma from all the stolen sweets and lies.

'Hi, Father.' He moved; as he proved to be still with us I continued, 'I didn't rob any sweets or tell lies.'

'Good child, good child,' says he, 'didn't you commit any sins at all then, love?'

'Oh, I did, Father,' I was delighted not to be disappointing him like.

'And what did you do, love?' he asked, humouring me, obviously.

'Well, Father,' said I, 'my mother hung my teddy bear out to dry on the line by the ears.'

'Oh,' says he greatly impressed.

'Well,' I said, 'when I saw the teddy hanging by the ears I got into a terrible temper and I shouted "Shit" at the top of my lungs.'

'Oh,' said he, 'and why did you say that terrible curse.'

'Well,' I explained, 'a lady near my Grandma's says if you shout "Shit" when you are in a temper you will never get a stroke from high blood pressure.'

'What is that lady's name?' he asked, conversational like.
'Oh,' said I, 'her name is Tits Murphy.'
He didn't answer. I could hear a laugh gurgling in his throat. In a very shaky voice he said:
'Say one Hail Mary for yourself and one for T . . . your friend.' With that he ran out of the box.
I ran out my side. He was outside shaking with laughter and a big red face on him.
He told Mother Brenda he would continue Confessions in a few minutes and practically ran into the Sacristy.
I knelt to say my penance and Tits' penance. Mother Brenda appeared at my side. 'What did you tell Father?' she demanded and her hands in two tight fists. I just looked at her blank and she walked away. She never found out what I told Father and for that she never forgave me. That failed to upset me I'm afraid.
I moved on up the classes. I worked myself into the ground to get good marks. I wrote with my left hand at home and my right hand at school. I followed the rules to a T. We were not allowed to mix with the boarders; we day scholars were not good enought to mix with them. If we met a nun on the corridors we had to stop and let her pass. There was room for ten nuns to pass, but, that was beside the point. When they came abreast with us we had to bow our heads. No matter how often a nun made game of you, one word — one look — and out the door with you.

My dad had a very good job and I was then allowed certain privileges. As long as he paid, that is. There were two operas each year. The cast was hand picked. Each member of the cast had to bring in £2 for costume hire and theaterical training. I could not sing a note but I was in every opera they put on. I had to stand in the chorus and mouth all the words and Daddy had to fork out £2 per trip. We also went on outings. We were also hand picked for this. You bring your own sandwiches and cakes and lemonade and £1. The outing was to the hockey field in the school grounds. The money was towards the Missions or the Building Fund or some such like. Each year in secondary we were given medals on ribbons to hang around our necks. These were supposed to be got on merit but once the £1 was brought in you got your medal.

If you didn't bring in your school fee within two days, you were disgraced. We were all brought into the hall and names read out as to who had not paid. They were asked why and had to answer in front of us all. That never happened me as I made sure they got their fee the same afternoon as we got the bill.

In secondary I was getting on great. I toed the line with the best of them. I did my homework and a bit extra for good measure. I paid attention in class. I was turning into a model pupil. I watched all the girls around me and saw some of them playing up to the nuns and that made me sick. I did my work and cleared out at home time. Some of the nuns tried to toady up to me but I was not having any of it.

Then I got into trouble. This day I was walking along the corridor on my way to the library. Our singing nun was coming towards me. I stopped, as was expected of me. Next thing just as she passed the huge May altar didn't she slip and fall on her back. The floor must have been wet or something. She sprawled and all I could see was her tartan knickers. I got into hysterics laughing instead of helping her up. She got up and marched me to Rev Mother's office for expulsion. Rev Mother read the riot act. She nearly devoured me and told me that I would be given another chance as far as expulsion was concerned. I was to weed the school cemetery she told me. This was the biggest punishment and the most degrading in her mind.

I went off to the cemetery like a boy with my little fork. The sun was shining and the birds were singing. I was weeding away at my dead ease and all of a sudden I heard it. The sound came from the grave in the shady corner — Rev Mother Theresa Collins 1912 read the headstone. It was heavy breathing, deathly heavy breathing, not quite natural like. I reckoned Rev Mother Theresa was on her way up and having being down since 1912 would be no beauty. I took to my heels and ran the half mile to the school. Harry, the gardener, caught me by the arm and I falling in the school yard.

'God,' said he, 'what is wrong with you?'. He shook me, as if I was not shook enough.

'I was doing punishment in the graveyard,' I told him. 'Rev Mother Theresa 1912 is coming up, I heard her breathing'.

'God,' said he, 'will you go away, that was naught but Rev Mother's old ass.'

I kept on panting but I looked stupid at him.

'Sheba - the old ass,' said he, 'come on and I will show you'. He led me back down the path I had come. Past the hockey fields, past St Bernadette's Grotto and past the hard courts. Sure enough Sheba was there to greet us. Harry and I sat, side-by-side, on Rev Mother Mary O'Brien's headstone while I caught my breath. I told him the cause of my punishment as we munched two red apples he had lifted out of the orchard. They were not the first red apples I had got from Harry. He was the blacksheep of one of the nun's families. Everyone maintained he was not right in the head. To my mind he was the sanest adult in that Convent. He certainly helped me keep my sanity during those trying times.

Our uniforms were another bogey with the nuns. We were made kneel down and if our pinafores were not two inches beyond our knees, home to Mother! My Mother had been a Domestic Economy Instructress before she married. Therefore, she was a topper with the needle. She took a passionate pride in our clothes. I had two uniforms every year. Not a speck of dirt was allowed on them and the two inch line was adhered to like a religion in itself. The nuns used take a peek under the skirts to see if we had the navy blue elastic at waist and knee knickers on, passion killers we used call them. If you were found in anything else, you were sent home with a note. A copy of that note was sent to the Pope, or that is the impression you were given. God, when I think of it. If the misfortunate nuns saw us 'girls' underwear now. Wow—they would think we were head hostesses in brothels. Come to think of it, I suppose that is one of the roles of marriage really. Goody!

Schooldays sped on. We were heading for the Inter-mediate. My father died. Rev Mother sent for me to sympathise on my loss. Her opening words were, 'Now, your good days are over, you will have no more fine feathers with him gone'.

The salt of my tears had burned the skin on my cheeks in the week of mourning that had preceded that interview. I could feel them smarting as she spoke. I knew what I would have to do without for the rest of my life.

It was not money — that could be earned again and again. It was not fine feathers as she called them. They could be bought. I had lost my Dad.

'Rev Mother,' I said quietly and I looked her straight in the eye, 'Rev Mother, let's not talk about him now, I've had enough'.

I turned from her white pasty face and walked out of the room. I held my head up high. I closed the door on her bitter face. I also closed the door on my childhood. From that moment I realised that I was an adult in an adult world.

I finished out that year like a robot. I do not remember doing the examination or anything about it. I did get it though.

I remember the last day I walked out those Convent gates. Harry was there to see me off. We shook hands and he too had tears in his old faded blue eyes as he looked at me. When I got home there was a red apple in my bicycle basket.

I can look back at those days now. I think of those nuns with fierce hatred in my heart. They say one should forgive one's enemies and those that do wrong to one. Especially, they recommend it if one is dying, like me. Yes, that is a lovely Catholic idea I think. I enjoy hating them though and anyway I am not dead yet. Maybe someday... but not today!

CHAPTER

4

As I walked into town the other day with my husband and children I looked at them with the impersonal eyes of a stranger. On the narrow path by the river's side there was only room for three to walk abreast. I walked behind them. There walked a man with pride, a modern man, a man of the seventies. His son walked with the same proud gait at his side. Another product of the seventies. God, he could do with a hair cut, I mused to myself. Still — he is young — the lads in his class at school are worse. Mary trotted beside them bubbling over as usual with life. God let her always bubble, I prayed to myself. From now on they will walk like that, just the three of them. As we walked along one or other of them would glance back and smile at me. They waited impatiently for the path to widen and we would all walk together. Days will come when they will come to the wide part of the path and they will have to walk alone. Out of pure habit they will look back — the path will be empty.

How many times have I turned, on a familiar path, and found myself alone? I can never listen to a seagull calling but memories stir like kicked ashes.

I cannot close the chapters of my childhood without paying tribute to my Dad. He was the backbone of our family all his life. When he died we fell to pieces like a filleted fish.

He was forever singing. I do not know whether he was a tenor or not. When he sang I did not question the key or the note — it was my Dad singing and that was that.

I can still see him striding around when we used be away at the seaside in the summers of my childhood. There he would be striding up and down Clay Castle in Youghal, down the strand in Dungarvan. Up and down hill he strode in Cobh. Swinging a blackthorn stick he'd be and he singing at the top of his voice.

His presence filled our house. Without seeing him you would know he was there. You would never fail to smell him anyway. He was never without a pipe in his mouth. He seemed to be forever lighting it and tapping it down. For years after his death I would cry inside in myself when I would smell his favourite tobacco with a stranger.

I, being the youngest, was his pet. He used to take me everywhere with him. All I would ever have to do was ask for something, anything, and it would be on my bed when I would wake up next morning.

He loved me with an undiluted love and in his eyes I could do no wrong. To him I was a constant source of amusement.

He used introduce me to all his friends and the pride and love used ring out in his voice for all to hear.

I loved all the attention I need not tell you. I was very small and frail looking. That along with two huge frightened eyes, and I was given bars of chocolate and bags of sweets.

Then I would arrive home to divide the spoils among my sisters. They were doing examinations at this stage, so could do with the extra energy. My mother used get worried and ask from whom I got the stuff.

'Joe,' I'd tell her or 'Jim' or whoever it might be.

Daddy would then fill her in on the occupation of the said gentleman – he could be anything from a bishop to a bin-man. All men were equal in my Dad's eyes and we had them all on first name terms.

I remember Mammy giving out to Tits Murphy about me taking sweets off Dad's pals. It used kill her that I had a face of a saint, full of innocence. She knew I was a lighting devil and wild into the bargain. Had she not spent five or six years in my company, she should know.

Tits had a theory on that. There was nothing she had not a theory on. 'No man,' she told my mother, 'chokes from eating out of a one's hand, no matter what age he or she is!' It took me years to cop that one on, but when I understood it, I couldn't agree more!

My Dad was always there to run to. He acted as a buffer between me and the world. Wild as I was I was very unsure inside. To have him in the background, a tower of strength, I could take on the world.

Afterwards the people he worked with told me they felt exactly the same. No matter what problem arose in the job he would straighten it out.

The summer I was fifteen he complained a bit about indigestion. He took no heed of it and we did not either. The warm sunny days stretched in a long, long hazy line. We walked and swam. He did seem a bit quieter but he was always like myself, a bit of a dreamer. He started to lose weight very fast. He continued to take spoonfuls of pepperminty powder after meals. He went off his food altogether.

He went to the local G.P. for a medical check-up. All his pals had ulcers and he maintained he was only joining the club.

They booked a bed for him in a Dublin hospital for a major operation. He had cancer in the gullet.

Then the nightmare nights started. For a night or two my mother's and my father's voices droned well into the small hours of the morning. Then for about four nights I could hear sobbing, the loud dry sobbing of my father, joined by my mother crying softly as she tried to comfort him.

My sisters were away in college and at work at this stage. At least they were saved that much.

I lay awake across the landing. I knew this great sorrow could only be between them. They were always so close, never apart — now this. I cried to myself for both of them in their grief.

Every so often one of them would gasp 'Don't wake Ellen, what are we going to do with her, she is only a child yet.'

I could hear them discussing my future and my mother's.

Each morning I would have to face them at breakfast. They ate and talked as if nothing was happening, that night again with the darkness would also come the tears.

I often wake suddenly and hear my father sobbing in the night, it is only a dream helped by the wind blowing around the house.

The day came for him to go to Dublin. The time came for him to leave. He kissed my mother. He kissed me. He pulled the front door shut after him. We stood in the bay window watching him go out to the waiting car. It was the

26

first time I saw his back hunched against early autumnal breezes. His head was bowed. With hands in his pockets he walked slowly past his favourite white rose tree. Past the michaelmas daisies.

I could not stand it any longer. I opened the front door and ran after him. I threw myself into his arms as I had done so often before.

'Will you be back Dad?' I asked. He looked at me. His brown eyes filled with tears. He shook his head. 'Mind your Mammy for me,' he said softly. He loosened my grip on him and walked out the gate. I never saw him again.

People called to help us over the few days after his funeral. Everyone did their best but it was no good really. I was amazed to see the sun shining, to hear the birds singing and life bustling around us as usual. Life, seemingly, had to go on. The days swept us along with them in a relentless rush.

The nights brought silence and darkness. Scalding tears led to utter exhaustion. Then sleep took over. The new dawn brought deeper realisation of our terrible loss.

No artist has been able to paint a broken, bleeding, crying out heart. No writer could ever describe it so what chance have I?

How in God's name can you put a broken heart down on paper?

People will tell you that time is a great healer? They did not lose my Dad.

CHAPTER

5

'What will I be when I grow up, Mammy?' my little girl asked me that again the other day. 'What would you like to be?' I asked. This question and answer has been tossed to and fro between us for years now. Instead of her usual list of a Nurse, a Doctor or a Mummy, she looked me straight in the eye and answered, 'What would you like me to be?'

I felt the tears prick my eyelids as I looked into her innocent brown eyes. Before me stood a little girl with flowing brown hair and pink cheeks from skipping. This is my daughter, I thought in awe, she is beautiful — she is so happy — Jesus, do not let me crack now.

'It does not matter what you choose to be,' I said, 'all I want is for you to be always happy.' I bent to pick up a knocked daffodil and she sped skipping past me down the path. 'I'll always be happy,' she laughed, 'always, and always and forever.'

I automatically unpegged the washing and brought it in. Life sweeps us on no matter what. Just the same as after my Dad died life swept me onwards.

Life swept me onwards. Where I was going I had not a clue but I just went with the tide. First I did a six month's crash course in a local Commercial College. That took every ounce of my concentration and energy.

My first office job was temporary prior to an examination and an interview with a committee of dishonest men.

I worked there for a good few months. Then I sat for the examination and was called to the interview. I came first in both. I lost the job. Strings were pulled for another girl and she got my job. My boss salved his conscience by giving me a fantastic reference. Practically all lies but very impressive. The last sentence reads (I still have it), 'This young lady has intelligence above average.' That I considered to be the *piece de resistance*! I would say the whole lot of them will rot in hell and I am very happy with the thought.

After that traumatic experience, I considered I needed

a little holiday. It so happened to be the height of the summer and my sisters were heading for Connemara to brush up their Irish.

My mother suggested that they take me with them. She had not finished her suggestion than I had a fist of knickers and a toothbrush in a bag. They were not too pleased, I'd say, but we got there.

They had to attend classes and lectures and they did numerous lines with the fellows there. I communed strictly with nature. I walked miles and miles alone. I contemplated painting a few pictures, but I was no use at art.

I contemplated writing a book, but that seemed out of the question too. One day I was standing on top of a very high cliff. Down below blue and white waves slashed off the rocks. Looking down into this water I contemplated suicide. I did not want to do away with myself or anything. I just fancied myself being washed in somewhere around the shore. There I'd be with my long hair floating on the water and my red and white birdseye dress showing up my smashing tan. A closer look at the rocks and that idea was cast aside. I knew one leap into the briny and my guts would be smashed out through my head in two minutes flat.

A whole gang from the Irish College, including my sisters, went into Galway three nights in a row. I was invited but declined. They were going in to see the picture *Gone with the Wind.* I stayed out in the wilds. I wanted to watch the sun go down on Galway Bay. They saw the picture three nights in a row. I saw the sun sink fourteen nights in a row, God knows, do you know? It is no wonder they wrote a song about it. It is absolutely breathtakingly beautiful.

When I had recharged my batteries after the two weeks, so to speak, I resumed my career.

Next stop was in another office as a mail order clerk. The previous mail order clerk had been in the job fifteen years. It took me fifteen minutes to brainwash the manager into thinking that I would be just as good, if not better. Ah, the confidence of youth!

I impressed him so much he left me off on my own from the word go. The orders rolled in from all over the country. They wanted beds, wardrobes, lino, carpet, you name it, we had it. They wanted it and they got it.

I replied to each one personally and signed his name. The stuff went flying out, 'up mountains and down dales,' wherever there was a road our van went. He was thrilled of course.

The letters with the orders were a panic. I always had a passion for writing letters and the job was a plum for me. Ones asking for beds told me their love life. Ones wanting prams asked for unusual names for babies. I replied as if they were all old friends.

After about two months, the manager called me to his office. He asked to see the letters and the copies of those I had sent out under his signature.

He spot checked a few of them, then a lady wanted him in the shop. He came back to me when she left.

'Do you know?' he said, pointing at the departing customer, 'she has named her new baby Charles, after me. It is all your fault.'

I sat and looked at him in silence.

'These letters,' he waved a fist of them, 'they are not businesslike at all.

If you cannot do the letters like Jenny (my predecessor) you will have to leave.'

'What have you there in your hand?' he asked.

'My sales graph, Sir,' I replied, handing it to him. Jenny's just happened to be with it, so I handed it over too. I had sensed trouble when I got his call. He studied the graphs. Then he looked at me. I looked him straight in the eye. He handed them back to me.

'Ellen,' he said, 'go back to your office and continue with the replies as you always do them — the customers seem to be happy.'

'Yes, Sir, thank you, Sir,' I replied respectfully and went back to my desk.

A few weeks later my mother spent a few months in the local hospital. I continued at work but cycled out to her every evening for a few hours. They eventually got her on her feet. The week before she was to be discharged there was fierce torrential rain for three days running. No coat would keep it out. Anyway, every time I went outside the

30

door I got soaked to the skin. I more or less dried my face and went about my business. Between rushing in and out to work, rushing meals for myself and tearing in and out to entertain my mother or have her entertain me, I was sweating. The soakings from the rain only helped to cool me off. The heel of the hunt was that I got a fierce cold and a cough. I felt like a maggot and a stepped-on one at that.

There was great excitement the day I brought her home. I spent a week or so fussing around her like an old hen. I was getting sicker and sicker. In I went to George for a bottle to put me on my feet. I was spitting blood at this stage, in pardon to you.

George stood in his surgery and just looked at me. I knew I looked like a badly re-heated corpse. My chest sounded like a melodeon and the ground felt soft. I slumped into his chair and looked at him silently. Then not to spare him any of the drama of my condition I got a black-out. I fell onto the floor and rolled under his desk.

Did I awaken to his dulcet tones and bedside manner? Like hell I did.

'What the bloody blazes have you being doing to yourself?' he shouted. To him I was still one of the neighbouring kids who spent my childhood spilling blood from numerous falls.

I got up with what dignity I could muster and swayed drunkenly over to the couch. He looked as if he was fit to kill me instead of cure me. Fortunately, I got a terrible fit of coughing and blood spattered out of my mouth, I must have looked like a blooming vampire.

X-rays showed that I had had pleuro-pneumonia on my feet, not just a lousy cold as I had though. George informed me that I would have to stay out of work for some months. One of my lungs was in a pretty bad state. I had to resign as a mail order clerk. The manager was genuinely sorry to see me go. He gave me a terrific reference, this time it was the truth. He told me that I was welcome to go back on his staff any time and he would find a place for me. My career had come to another halt.

Me and my mother were convalescent together. We had a great time comparing notes on our symptoms and lazing around the place. She made a fantastic recovery, thank God, and so did I.

For months I had a tremendous cough. It was real weird. If you could imagine a cross between the roar of a wild boar being slaughtered slowly in his senses and a box of mad dogs barking their heads off, you would have a fair idea of it.

At long last George gave me permission to continue with my career. I answered an advertisement for a typist/receptionist in the local paper. I was called for interview. Before I got to the front door with its brass plates and shiny knocker I had to go up about a dozen steps. The offices were in one of our old Georgian houses.

I was met by the receptionist and introduced to the secretary. She filled me in on duties and office hours while we waited for the boss to interview.

He rang down for me and I went off to his office. His plushy carpet felt gorgeous under my feet. He turned out to be a nice old man in his sixties. He told me all the qualifications necessary for the job! Honours Leaving Certificate, fantastic speeds in shorthand and typing, years of experience in filing and reception. God love him, sure he had not a hope of getting a one like that.

I did not tell him that though. I told him all about my lack of education, lack of speeds and lack of experience. He limped over to the filing cabinet and I told him my grandmother's cure for rheumatism. Well, he said he had a rheumatic hip when I asked him. We chatted away and I told him about my lung to console him like.

In the middle of this his secretary arrived with his elevenses. He caught me looking at his cup of steaming hot coffee. He had a grand fat chocolated-coated, silver-wrapped biscuit with it.

'Are you hungry?' he asked looking at me for the first time.
'God, I'm starved,' said I.
I drank his coffee and ate his biscuit and agreed to start work the following Monday.
The first day I was first in, the doors were not even opened. The secretary was delighted to see me so keen. She introduced me to the other girls and settled me in my place.

I was to act as receptionist, answer the phone and do an odd bit of typing. There seemed to be droves of fellows floating around but I was too busy to take much heed of them.

Mid-morning the secretary congratulated me on my work so far. Then she took me upstairs to introduce me to the rest of the staff. We went into a huge office where there seemed to be about half a million men. She called for silence and said to all and sundry. 'Gentlemen, this is Ellen, our new girl.' There was a voice shouted, 'Things is looking up around here at last.' 'Such grammar', she shouted at him. Then she withered him with a look.

I think I shook hands with them all and they looked at me with keen interest. Now at the time I was not a bad looking bird. Remember I was in the prime of my youth. Still I felt I should not encourage them so I gave them a wan smile.

On the way down to my office I was given a lecture on the behaviour expected in the office. There was to be no hanky-panky between male and female members of the staff. There was to be no horse-play. There was to be no loud shouting on the stairs or in the offices. I was told that there was nothing to fear from those fellows because if one fellow went out of line he would be sacked.

I wouldn't have to go up to that office anyway to take dictation as the other two girls were there for that. I felt that she felt that I felt that if I were to go up and work in that office, I would feel like a feminine edition of Daniel in the Lions Den! That is complicated, I know, but I am sure you get my meaning. I know I stood there and gave that impression but sure for God's sake, aren't I a born actress!

I settled into the routine of the office and the time flew. My two months probation were up and I became a permanent member of the staff. I got on great with the other two girls. They told me hair-raising stories of escapes they had to make from the amorous advances of the lads upstairs.

Then one of the girls left to get married. I was offered her job. I took it and started training in a new receptionist.

One day I was upstairs and I was thinking to my self that whatever bit of sex appeal I had was gone. All of a sudden one fellow threw his arms around me in a passionate embrace. I looked around at the rest of them. They were going on with their work as if the passionate tableau in front of them was invisible.

I got a fierce fright – honest to God, I did. I daren't shout 'Rape' because the boss had a bad heart. One roar like that would finish him. And it might encourage my friend!

I stood my ground. Your man thought I was encouraging him to prove his prowess as a lover. He hugged me tighter against him. I was not well enough, at the time, for such an onslaught of love. I gave a chain of lung-tearing heart-and-head splitting coughs. All thoughts of sex were forgotten. My attacker nearly died with the fright! The audience immediately jumped into action. They got me water, they got me cough sweets and they completely forgot about the letters I was to type in the first place.

For the rest of my stay in the job, that young man carried my bike up and down the office steps - four times a day. Another lad used to post the letters for me. We had to clock in each morning at 9.30. I was never registered as ever being late. In fact I was never in time after the first few months. They used forge my name in the book and I could duck in then, more or less at my leisure.

I got to know all their troubles. Any rows with girlfriends or wives and in they would come to my office. Between us we would straighten out the trouble.

In that job there was fierce output of work. The whole staff worked as a team and we had the satisfaction that we were being well paid for our work. Each Christmas we got our bonus. There was an annual rise for everyone.

I did not have much to do with the boss except when his secretary went for her annual holidays. I used enjoy working with him. On one such occasion he had the misfortune to ask me was I happy in the job. I said I was but that I was leaving in twelve months' time. I showed him my day old engagement ring.

I told him I wanted to ask him something. He said, ask away. I asked him for a two pound a week rise. I explained that I was half an orphan and that I fancied the idea of having £100 of a dowry. He agreed at once. I thought he would fire me but I felt I should take the chance.

When the time came for me to leave the lads and the girls contributed towards a wedding present for me and my husband-to-be.

The secretary told me how much they had so that I could choose whatever I liked in town. I had seen a fantastic bedspread and eiderdown set and they had just enough money. Three years practically to the day I had walked into the office for the first time I walked out for the last. My career-girl days were over but I was looking forward to the next chapter in my life — Marriage.

CHAPTER

6

When I look at our two children these days, I worry terribly about them. What does the world hold for them? Will the good influence their father and I have over them now last them a lifetime? Will they have sufficient a bank balance of happiness in their hearts to dip into when the times come hard? They say no man is an island, God, I do not know that now. I think that everyone walks alone to a certain extent. I do not think that it is any joke either. Maybe it is because I feel kind of depressed at the moment. I should be ashamed not to be grateful for the happiness I have had, but sure I am only human!

Since I was born I have been wrapped in a cocoon of love. My father and mother completely spoilt me. To them I was a novelty and a most unexpected bonus to an already united and what they had thought complete family.

To my sisters I was better than any doll they ever had. They fought like tigers to dress me, do my hair and take me out walking. Our friends and relations doted on me. Outside of school I had friends, both boys and girls, whom I loved and they loved me. I knew no other emotion only love and returned every ounce I got.

Of course, when I went to school I met my match — for the first time I was not petted. The nuns took an instant dislike to me and I got a fierce shock. I soon learned to adjust to their injustice and served out my years in their company. I was not the only one victimised but could see no reason for such hatred. Naturally I hated them back and carried on with my life.

There was also someone else for me to love. God, I have always been mad about Him. To me, God was always, and still is, like an old Uncle. One I have never met face to face yet. Very lovable but terrible eccentric! All these years we have got on marvellously well together. We seem to have a great understanding. Granted all our conversations have been one-sided, but I have a feeling He has enjoyed them every bit as much as I have.

All my life I have had a man beside me to hold my hand and help me over life's milestones. When I come face to face with Death I wish to be completely alone. I want no one watching me. All my life nothing has come easy to me. I have had to fight for everything I have. My achievements have been tiny but I am proud of them. I wish to meet Death with dignity. I shall whisper, 'Jesus , will you hold my hand?' And I know He will.

The little boys I played with grew up and spilled into my girlhood. All my girlfriends were having a ball. They were playing spin the bottle and dares and exchanging kisses for apples, books, any excuse. Overnight, it seemed, the mud splashed kids had watered down hair, long pants and were Don Juaning it all over the road.

From as far back as I can remember, I decided I would get married. That was my life's ambition. Anything else was in the halfpenny place! With all these young men around I felt very confused. I needed time and a clear view of what was happening. Of course, it would take me to complicate things for myself. Not for me were stolen kisses. Yerra, not at all. I mentally gave myself a shake and set out a few rules. I produced a mental yardstick by which to live up to.

First and foremost I was going to bounce up to the altar a virgin. I was having no one pulling and dragging at me for dares or spinning bottles. I was, as I grandly told my pals, 'sparing myself for my husband.' The girls reaction to this was fantastic. They warned me my popularity would wane in no uncertain fashion. I would finish up an old maid, they warned me, or worse than that I would end my days as a nun. What a hope!

My life, I told them, was mapped out before me. Somewhere along my path there would be someone special. It could be one of our childhood friends or someone completely new. I would meet him and stay with him for the rest of my life. They questioned my sanity and suggested that I get sense and enjoy myself now. No, I was willing to let them off to their games of make-believe-love. I was saving my energy for a future date. If this man of my dreams failed to succumb to my charms, I'd need to be as fresh as a daisy to change his mind.

As the days and years passed, my boyfriends multiplied. I had an air of mystery it seemed. They found my attitude towards them fascinating. Absolutely fascinating! They took me for walks and to the pictures. They weeded and cut the grass in my mother's gardens. I used to do a few gardens for old people who lived near us. These people were crippled and had been very good neighbours. I had only to appear with a lawnmower or a shopping basket and there was always some fellow there to lend a hand. Sometimes two!

Any amorous advances were gently ignored. If they persisted, I'd tell them cut it out. If that failed to stop them, I'd give them the father and mother of a thump! I'd warn them first of course. I could listen for hours to their dreams, their hobbies and their worries. To them I was a cross between a sister and a rather senile granny I think. I used write compositions for them. That was one thing I shone at at school. I'd hear their lessons, anything — except, no messing!

One summer five of these boyfriends called, one after the other, to our house. They came to say good-bye, they were going away as priests. They had been doing lines on and off with my girlfriends. Their going out of circulation was a great shock to the girls. I, of course, got blamed. I ruined these lads, one of the girls told me: 'Yourself and your bloody mental chastity belt!' she roared at me. The boys went off and eventually got ordained. One of them, the most passionate youth I ever thumped, is now a Bishop in America! I remember the day he called, round collar and all. He was about six feet tall and one foot wide. He was flying to America that day.

'May I kiss you good-bye, Ellen?' he said and my mother and his mother there as an audience.

'No, Lanky,' that was what we called him, 'some day when you are a Bishop I'll kiss you,' I promised.

I thought our paths would never again cross. His mother died and he had no ties with our town. Faith they did though — only last month too.

My husband and I were at a social. There was a huge convention of bishops and the like on in the town the same week. In the start of the night we were all told about the guests of the night, real V.I.P. seemingly. This American Bishop would give a short talk and no knowing to the number of letters he had after his name, etc., etc., etc., His name was mentioned, time and time again. I never get names right, I always get them 'arseways' as Tits used to say!

Anyway, he arrived. All fifteen stone of him — a huge man. God bless him. We listened to his speech. The crowd were falling over themselves to get near him and to impress him. I, as usual, stayed on the outskirts. Then it was suggested that we all kiss his ring. We got into line and I took time to study him. Under the rolls of flesh and all the grandeur I recognised him.

When I got on a level with him I pretended to trip over my maxi. Your man lent over to assist me, gallant to the last. As soon as his ear was on a level with my face I whispered. 'You can kiss me now Lanky!'

God tonight! I got terrorised he would get a stroke. Two big red spots came in his cheeks and he seemed to sway a little. 'Jesus,' I prayed to myself, 'don't let him die or they will kill me.'

He straightened up to his full height — he looked about eight feet tall to me. He looked me up and down and bellowed, 'I will not, I do not want another black eye like the last time.'

The crowd around us thought he had gone stark raving mad. The ring kissing queue broke up and watched us from a safe distance.

Thank God the band then struck up. Me and Lanky led the floor in the first waltz.

Now, I have gone off on a tangent again. Trying to co-ordinate my home life, my school life, my career and my love life is worse than trying to knit a jersey! It reminds me of the fair isle jerseys my sisters used to knit me. All the colours dropping in and out. Joining each other again and again at regular intervals. If you could bear with me, with this in mind, we would be in business. Yes, now I have it. Consider this book as a big piece of fair isle. Then I can also keep the main trend going at the same time. Just like the main colour in fair isle that will be my straight story.

There will be loads of yellow for laughter, grey for tears, and purple for passion (marital, of course) and what book is without purple passages! I thrive on them.

Back to my love life, my pets! Did I meet the man of my dreams? I did. It all happened in the local skating ring. I had gone in with a girlfriend to look for her sister. I had never been in there before. I stood by the barrier fascinated at the scene. An old man, like a little gnome, romped away on an electric organ. Boys and girls waltzed around on skates. More boys and girls sat around in seats and watched. I idly took in all the action. My friend saw her sister and joined her and a few lads. They called me over but I stayed put. Across the floor from me was a little shop where they hired out skates.

Then I saw a boy come in and stride up to the shop. He was tall and dark and carried himself with pride. He hired a pair of skates and put them on.

As if an unseen hand was pushing me I moved towards the shop. I hired a pair of skates and strapped them onto my shoes. I had never worn a pair of skates in my life. Do you think that for a moment that deterred me? Not at all.

I kept my eye on my man. He hadn't gone far. He was on the slippery floor chatting up a dark one with glittery brown eyes.

I leaned nonchalantly against the railings and waited. He chatted on and on. To move I would have had to skate—I couldn't skate, therefore I daren't move. He swirled out onto the floor and did a few rounds of it then he came back —to the one with the glittery eyes. I waited another while. I was in no hurry — the skates were hired for two hours!

Out of the corner of my eye I saw him gaze over once or twice — rather uninterested I thought. The next time he looked over I turned and looked him straight in the face. My face was the picture of innocence as I looked into his eyes. In my heart I was screaming silently.

'Jesus, are you listening? That is him — will You do something!'

Five minutes later he came over and asked me to skate. One minute later we were both full length on the floor. We got up and fell again within a matter of minutes.

'I cannot skate at all,' I said. I decided I was going to start life with this fellow on a very honest basis.

'I'll teach you,' he promised and off we went.

I curved my body into his arms, I left my freshly shampooed hair brush across his face, I rested my cheek against his for fleeting seconds now and again. All the ones in all the love books I had read used those tricks. I was taking no chances. He kept his promise — he taught me to skate.

He taught me to live and to love. He taught me how to appreciate poetry, painting, music, nature, everything. Over the years, of course, not just then!

Before I met him I knew there was something missing — since I met him I have become a real person.

About two months before I met him, I started doing a Perpetual Novena to Our Lady in one of our local Churches. This was on every Saturday night. When I started dating him on Saturday nights I had to choose between him and the Novena. I had not time for both as I had to be in at nine o'clock. I'm afraid Our Lady got hammered! I explained to her my absence though. I told her I considered my prayers were more than answered and that I was not abandoning her and thanked her profusely for her help.

I was never, and still am not, a great one for Novenas or the like. I feel closer to God when I am alone and haven't a crowd around me distracting me. Even at Mass my mind wanders and I find myself pricing all the clothes on the ones around me. I'd be comparing my children with other children and noting their clothes so that I can copy them at a later date. Digging in the garden or scrubbing the floor, that is where I pray. That is also where I curse, but that is beside the point.

After a few months of constant dating I felt that my fate was sealed. I would have loved to have eloped there and then and have it all over and done with. We were too bloody young to marry. I still had to finish out at school. He had to finish out at college and get a job.

There was a span of years stretching ahead of us before we could marry. He naturally did not mention marriage. It probably did not strike him at all. Needless to mention, I had not a notion of saying anything. From our conversations

I gleaned from him what attributes he considered necessary for a wife.

The woman of his dreams would have to be bloody versatile to say the least of it. She would have to be able to cook like his mother. She would have to be able to knit like his mother. She would have to look and act like an angel and at the same time run his home, rear his children (beautiful of course), be his private nurse, maid, nanny and mistress.

Faced with that list now I would enter a convent and just throw my hat at the whole lot. But, I was younger then. With the wild abandon of youth I took up the challenge. I was going to train myself to be a model wife. I bought wool and knitting needles. I ate, drank and slept with them for ages before I mastered the knack of purling and plaining perfectly. Casting on and casting off I went until I was nearly black in the face.

He kept appearing in jerseys his mother had knit for him and that nearly drove me worse mad. They were perfect!

We cycled miles on picnics. His mother packed his saddie bag with delicious little cakes and apple tarts. I brought dainty little sandwiches cut in fancy shapes and no crusts. They made a terrible laugh of me at home. My normal idea of a sandwich up to then was two door-steps of bread and butter with stuff hanging out of them at all angles. All of a sudden I was gone all dainty. I spent hours in front of my mirror trying, in vain, to get an angelic expression on my face. I joined the Technical School for cooking. I covered the whole course for four years. I finished up in the Cordon Bleu Class. I was so attentive the teacher asked me in the end was I sitting for some very important examination. I told her I was not. But, I was really. I was trying to pass as a model cook. They say the way to a man's heart is through his stomach don't they?

I made sure he walked me home every cookery class night and sampled my culinary efforts. Himself and my mother used tuck in like a pair of wolves and they would not talk to me until they had eaten every scrap of my class work. She is a terrific cook herself and even she was impressed. I just waved off their compliments airily.

For our second Christmas I presented him with a hand

knitted sweater. It would have got a prize in any Irish Horse Show. It was perfect. I was amazed that all the blood, sweat and tears I shed over it did not show. He presented me to his family. I think they were more impressed with the jersey. His mother had to be persuaded that it was not knit on a machine. His father ordered her to knit him an identical one without fail. His brothers put in their orders too. The poor woman was badgered from all sides. I took note that by marrying him I would acquire three brothers and a young sister, none of which I ever had before.

His family took to me immediately. They treated me as if I was one of themselves. It was taken for granted that I had come into the house and that from then on I was going to be around for quite a while. If I had not been premature, I would be exactly the same age as one of his brothers. I had the misfortune to tell him this one day. Now no matter where we are he pipes up with this information. I cut at least ten years off my age and no one questions me. Then your man comes up with our birthday date and year and I have to drown his voice. If he persists I shall have to drown him.

I was always a great romancer. I believed that, behind every great man there was a woman. I felt that if I were to marry my man, I would be a fantastic help to him. I persuaded myself that without me he would not be happy. He would know that I was behind him cheering him on to greater things. It was my job in life to marry him and only him.

Before he proposed I had three proposals from my childhood friends. These had left school and got jobs. They were very lucky and were going abroad for a few years. Each one felt about me like I felt about my husband-to-be. I refused them.

Oh, I don't know. Maybe he would have been happier married to someone else. Maybe I would. I doubt it though; for me, I mean. By dying now I am giving him another chance. He is still young enough to get married again. Our children are young enough to fit in with a new mother. They are also old enough not to forget me. I hate the idea of being forgotten — vanity thy name is woman and all that!

One of the happiest days of my life was the day he proposed to me. After all my waiting I said, 'I suppose I might!' At long last I had come of age.

CHAPTER

7

Every Saturday there are weddings in the Church near our home. For the past years the children have been fascinated by the various groups who have gone in and out. The big weddings have appealed no end to Mary. She is just full of romance. As each couple move off she invariably remarks, 'Now they will live happily ever after.' 'Please God,' I always pray silently to myself. I hope that when my two come down from the altar they will walk off with their life partners with the same confidence as I did.

Ever since I was a very little child I dreamed of having a white wedding. A long white dress would sweep the floor. A long white lacy veil would be held by a pretty little flower girl. My bridesmaids, a full row of them, would be dressed in the pastel shades of sweet pea flowers. My groom and all the other men would be in tails.

When my Dad died our washing machine was sold. Our car was sold. My mother was left a large sum of money which had to last her for the rest of her life. I could have got around her and had a white wedding with all the trimmings but I had not the heart. I decided to have a quiet wedding.

A few of my friends were getting married that same summer. I joined in and enjoyed the excitement of a white wedding, kind of second hand, if you like.

Visiting their homes during this period was a constant source of entertainment for me. The villains of these fireside comedies were their fathers. At the mention of eighty-odd guests these lovely men's faces would turn a very dangerous shade of purple. Their hands would stray to the area of their chests. One would be left to wonder if they were experiencing a pain in their hearts or their wallets.

Not alone, they were told, had they to fork out for the wedding. They were also expected to throw a pre-wedding party. These fellows were more in the humour to throw a fit!

The sweetest most docile of fathers nearly went beserk

at the mere mention of tails. They roared and ranted like wild, unleashed tigers. They would not dream of being found dead, laid out in or buried in tails. Through all these discussions there was a faint suspicion of murder or suicide. As the brides-to-be discussed trouseaus, cakes, flowers, priests and churches, their old men fumed in their chairs. They threatened to wash their hands of the whole affair, they went silent, they refused point blank to be drawn into these important discussions. Their points of view were not even missed. The mothers and daughters went on planning regardless. Nothing bar an atom bomb or a fall out would save the poor misfortunate breadwinner in the corner.

You could read these men's thoughts as they looked at their loving families, who looked as if they were endeavouring to put them all in the poor house. Was this the baby he rocked to sleep? Was this the baby he taught to walk? To cycle? Was this the one who wore out two records of Annie Frind's Nuns' Chorus? How many times had he to listen to that record? How many times? HOW MANY? Now he was going mad! Definitely! No sooner was the last note of the millionth time still echoing in his brain than your one started going around in a daze. She no longer fancied herself walking in the cloisters with her veiled sisters. No, she didn't! Now she was onto another hobby-horse altogether — a more expensive one. She was expecting him to part with his life's savings, well practically; it was his sweat and blood anyway. The white ensemble would be used only on the one day. His suit would be back in the Clothes Hirers shop the following day. The eighty-odd breakfasts would be all in eighty-odd stomachs in less than one hour. What would he have in the end? What would she have? Memories. A fistful of photographs and an empty wallet.

The mothers were much worse in their approach. They were determined to salt their husbands for the last penny. Some of them never stopped about their husbands meanness. They kept on and on at them. In the end I was on the men's sides. Months after the big swish weddings these same women were still cribbing. Now they were feeling the pinch and they did not like it.

Talking to those brides in a few years was really an

eye opener. They thought no more of their parents than if they had not spent a penny on them. They still had the clothes from the big day and none of them had touched or looked at them since. Each one told me quietly, over a cup of tea, she wished she had her choice again. They would have used the money on carpets or furniture or the down payment on a car. One of them had two sets of twins in quick succession and swore none of her four daughters would have a white wedding. She would buy each of them an electric washer instead!

My little daughter now dreams of a white wedding. If it means taking all our savings, I am afraid her dream will not come true. If she has a nice, quiet wedding, it will not mean that we love her any less. God grant her the sense to realise this. Still it is a long way off. Maybe she will trip up to the altar in the lacy creation of my childhood dreams. Maybe she will have a pretty little flower girl. I hope her dreams come true. No matter what she wears she will be the most beautiful bride anyone has ever seen.

As the time for my wedding drew near I was getting real excited. I shopped for my trousseau and added to my bottom drawer. I bought little things now and again and saved them like Scrooge. Nearly every night I would take a look into a big old trunk I had. I would handle all the little things I had bought and got and dream of my future.

My wedding day dawned at long last. A coolness and calmness descended on top of me. I was ready hours before anyone. I was watering my mother's potted plants and the rest of them were rushing around me like lunatics. With about an hour to spare I took a slip off her geranium and set it in a pot. I still have it on my kitchen window-sill!

At long last the taxi arrived and I was off. When we arrived at the church the sun came out and shone brilliantly on top of us. My sisters were rushing around still.

On account of not having my Dad, one of my brothers-in-law was to give me away. We set off up the aisle in great style. When we came on a level with his wife, my sister, he left my side. He genuflected and knelt down beside her out of pure habit. I looked at him for a moment. Then I gathered myself and went on up to the altar. Alone. My brothers-in-law-to-be noted my dilemma and nearly got hysterics at the situation. So did I. My husband-to-be knelt at the altar and I joined him.

The ceremony was short. It was performed by a priest who had been a friend of the family for years. We then took the usual photographs and adjourned to the hotel for our breakfast.

All through the wedding ceremony and all through the breakfast I could feel the weight of my wedding ring on my finger. I would steal glances at it and then look around and catch my husband's eye. I really could not believe that my dream had come true at long last. It did not matter to me about the long white dress or the veil. All that mattered to me was that I was at last married to the only man I had ever loved. I couldn't wait for my life to really begin. I felt like singing, shouting or screaming with sheer happiness. Instead I sat and talked quietly to everyone. I coolly bade them all good-bye. I placed my hand in my husband's and turned to move off with him. I could take on the whole world — I had him by my side.

CHAPTER

8

These days when the children are at school and my husband at work I often sit alone and think. I often wonder at the foolishness of people grasping for the moon. God knows we all get notions of grandeur and dream dreams but now in the eleventh hour I am getting sense! I would love a few weeks in Spain — the four of us — Venice, Rome; you name it and I would go. I have seen very little of the world actually. I never craved to travel to the extent that by not going I was miserable. But I would have gone at the drop of a hat. To sit in our own back garden with ice cold lemonade was heavenly to me. The four of us could have been anywhere in the world and be just as happy. It amazes me that that feeling of unity has always been between us ever since we were only a twosome. The children have only added to this feeling of oneness we seem to have cemented our lives with.

Months before we got married my husband had booked our honeymoon. No where else would do us only Paris, the city of lovers. My father-in-law mentioned that we could, if we felt like it, bring him back loads of cheap cigarettes from the duty free shop at the airport. This meant buying them before we left Ireland, taking them to Paris and bringing them back. As neither of us smoked we decided to do it.

On arriving at the Paris airport we discovered knowing the language would be an advantage. My husband had no French and I had rusty Intermediate Cert quality. The Custom's Officer did not care tupence if the pen of our aunt was in the garden nor that there was a man at the door with a parcel in his hand. All he wanted to know was why we had four hundred cigarettes more than our quota. However, I also discovered that the Frenchman are like the Irishman in one way. They cannot resist a pair of filled-up eyes. We passed on. I repaid him in full with a lovely, but still sorrowful, smile. I had had my teeth cleaned by my dentist the week previous and felt, at that stage, it was money well spent.

We recovered from our brush with the customs and made for our hotel in a taxi. We handed our hotel card to the driver and said nothing. He drove us through a string of streets at break-neck speed. All that worried me was that we would be killed and see nothing of this beautiful city.

Eventually, in about three minutes flat, or so it seemed, we stopped outside our hotel. We went in and were met by a dapper little man with gold fillings in his teeth. He spoke exquisite English and we signed the register. Having left the bags in our room we went out into the sunshine.

Paris was ours for two whole weeks. We were very new to it all and rather nervous. We used the Metro all the time and maps which my husband is a wizard at following. He did all the directing and I did all the talking. We dashed here and we dashed there. We found quaint little markets and antique shops and rummaged among book shops in the back streets. We went up Eiffel Tower and saw all the famous buildings from the air. I am not a great person for heights but I did not notice being up so high there. I had Paris at my feet. We visited each of these places in turn and revelled in their beauty. Notre Dame was according to the book 'an exquisite example of Architecture,' to me it was just another corner of Heaven. We knelt at the Unknown Soldier's Grave at the Arc de Triumphe. We went up all the steps of Sacre Coeur and found it breathtakingly lovely.

Napoleon's Tomb was the most impressive war memorial we saw but there were many others which marked the French people's love and admiration for their leaders of bygone days. We spent a day at Versailles where the gardens really are beyond description.

In Paris you can really feel that you are threading on ground that has been trodden on before many, many years ago. The city is steeped in history. As my husband is very interested in history I got a personally guided tour. I learned more by actually seeing these places than ever I did reading about them. One would envy the American and English children who were on guided educational tours. They were soaking up the history on the very ground on which it was made.

For our meals we used use the Self-Service Restaurants

and we had no language problems. Sometimes for the novelty we would go Bohemian. We would buy a french loaf. These are about three feet long. Armed with that and a bottle of wine we would dine in style under the famous bridges of Paris.

There were French tramps called hoboes with prams with all their possessions beside them. They cooked lobsters or other fish on open fires along the quays. Others, having dined and wined, were lying full length on the ground fast asleep, without a care in the world. They would be filthy with the dirt and their clothes in tatters. In their eyes there was a look of content and happiness one could not help but envy. One would feel, as one passed by them, that one was encroaching on their privacy. When any one of them would look up at us they never failed to bid us 'Bon jour'. Their peaceful smiles were like a benediction.

After tea we visited the night clubs and dance halls. These nights on the town were most enjoyable and most expensive. The clubs were full of nudes. They stood like statues around the stages. They swung on swings and appeared hanging out of the ceiling in baskets. And not a tack of clothes on them. I was thankful to God I had not brought any of my maiden aunts. They would have died the death at the cut of the ones.

One night we were at one of these nudey shows and one of the girls got a fit of sneezing. Before they had finished they were all nearly sneezing. I daresay from exposure. If I had a figure half as good as them I would never wear a stitch of clothes again in this life — or in the next!

On our last night in Paris we stayed out of doors. We sat on the steps of Sacre Coeur and watched the twinkling lights of this fabulous city. Lovers strolled hand-in-hand. A boy strummed a guitar on the steps above us. The music floated on the night air. It seemed to gather the sadness of the wars of long ago. The splendour of the beautiful buildings around us melted into the strains of the melody. It went from the luxurious clubs to the squalour of the back streets. It carried on including the smiles of the tatty old men and the merry shrieks of the children playing in the streets.

There was a very old man beside us. When I looked at

him I saw unashamed tears glistening on his withered cheeks. He started to hum away to himself. Then slowly, very slowly his humming gathered momentum. With the natural ease of a born singer he broke into song. The first bars of *Santa Lucia* floated into the soft warm, scented air. His voice was hesitant at first. Then it soared on the night air like a bird left out of a cage.

When he finished there was a hush. Not a sound could be heard on the now packed steps. Then shouts of 'Encore, Bravo,' went into the night. The old tenor gathered his raggy clothes around his boney frame. He ambled down the steps with the applause floating down after him.

The crowd soon dispersed and the boy with the guitar bade us 'Bon soir.'

We were left alone — just the two of us — the lights of Paris still twinkled. Sacre Coeur stood in all its majesty behind us. The *Santa Lucia* echoed in our hearts.

Hand in hand we walked back to the hotel and into the future. Our honeymoon was over — very soon we would have to face the reality of marriage. I knew that no matter what was in store for us we would survive. We could never say we were poor, never say we had not lived — not with the memories of those two weeks locked in our hearts.

CHAPTER

9

Each day before I start on my little writing stint I clean our home. I still look at the carpets and furniture with awe. The beautiful pictures we have gathered over the years. The hundreds of books and records. Slowly but surely we gathered all these things around us. The gardens have been a constant joy to us. We look on them as an extension to our house. The back garden in particular is just an outdoor room in the summer. If these material things were to be taken off us in the morning — we would not feel the loss. Looking back I know that what extra happiness we have now than we had when we started in this house was not gained from these possessions.

People will tell you that if you take just one beautiful, intelligent and hard-working girl and get her married, you have a completely different kettle of fish in a few years. She will turn into a cabbage, as sure as a hairy, crawly caterpillar will turn into a beautiful butterfly. Maybe I was not beautiful, intelligent or hard-working enough to begin with. Maybe I did not marry the right man. I do not know. I have hardly had time to turn around in the past sixteen years. If there are still young and innocent ones hoping that marriage is a state of life in which you can 'measure out your life in coffee spoons', as the man said, God, they are in for a fierce land!

When we arrived home from our honeymoon, I expected a roll of drums to greet us. What a hope. When we landed at our new semi-detached, the builder informed us it was not ready yet. But, he told us, move in by all means.

If the Palm Court Orchestra did not exactly herald our entrance in along the yet untiled hall, we had plenty of music. There was singing in the master bedroom while the painter finished the paintwork. There was whistling from the garage while a fellow plastered the walls. Hammering and drilling resounded all over the house.

The builder escorted us around. Ignore the men, he told us. They would not interfere with us at all. For weeks one of them could appear at your elbow like magic between the hours of eight in the morning and five in the afternoon. Needless to mention, any dancing of the seven veils or ardent love-making, with one's life partner, of course!, had to be executed between the hours of five in the evening and eight in the morning.

We were in the house two weeks when we decided to have high tea for my in-laws. This was to take place after five, of course. I had our new table gone bandy legged from all the stuff. I had cream-filled flans and tarts, numerous cakes and savories and God knows what. It was my first time entertaining them and I was going to impress on them what a great bargain they acquired into their bosom. The years at the Technical School really did the trick — such a beautiful table, even though I say so myself. If I work to accomplish doing an art — cooking, sewing or anything and it is a success, I tell everyone. I am not a bit modest that way.

I took a private tour around the house. The scrubbed boards shone in the summer sunlight. The windows twinkled Some of our stuff was still at my mother's and some at his. Still it was home. With all our presents and bought furniture we would not have it full for ages. I would not go into debt for anyone. To me there are no Joneses and never were. I love to sleep nights and if I owed money I'd toss and turn all night. I swore that day that we would build up our possession slowly and relish each room as it was done. We did just that. It took years but it was terrific.

I romanced around from one room to the next. This would always be our bedroom, I mused to myself. I'd love a baby boy first and then a girl a few years later. She would have him to fight her fights for her. He could take her to a few dances and break the ice for her later. She would always have him to stand up for her in later life.

I looked out at the gardens. We would cultivate them beautifully. The prams would go in the cosy sunny corner. The children would romp on the lawn. We would sunbathe to our heart's content. High hedges would give us a private, beautiful, outdoor world just for the four of us.

All of a sudden a bloody big crow went to the toilet

right across the back bedroom window. I ran off and got an old knickers. I always use them as dusters and floor cloths. Armed with this piece of underwear, I jumped out the window. Real agile I was. I stood outside on the narrow window ledge. I scrubbed and rubbed at the dirt. At last I had the window shining once again. Then I had the misfortune to look down. The garden looked very far away, the ledge felt very small. I closed my eyes for a split second.

When I reopened them I found myself in a narrow grave-like hole in the garden, I presumed. This is like the Valley of Shadows, I told myself, to cheer myself up like. The sun got shadowed and a figure appeared above me. Is this Death, I wondered? I have a great imagination, but it will really be the death of me one of these days! As the figure bent more I got a better look. Death, I told myself cheerfully, did not appear in a maroon and grey jersey. And I doubted if he wore a grey cloth cap. The figure spoke to me:

'What in Jesus Name did you go and do that for Missus?' said he.

I recognised him then; he was the watchman and his name was Paddy.

'I fell out the window, I think,' I told him.

'Indeed you did,' said he, 'I seen you. Is anything broke?'

'I don't think so,' I said, but I was not too sure as I couldn't move anyway in the constricted area.

He caught me by the two hands and levered me out of the trench.

'You are not dead anyway,' he noted as I stood up in front of him on my two grand legs. They felt like two jam sandwiches actually, real fluffy ones at that.

'Can you walk?' he asked.

I took a few tentative steps towards my house to demonstrate my prowess and he seemed quite satisfied.

'Well, Jesus,' he said, conversational like, 'if I found you dead in that gas pipe trench, I would have dropped dead in on top of you.'

'That would be lovely,' I commented, 'we would be like a modern version of Romeo and Juliet — imagine the headlines in the local paper.'

The idea really appealed to Paddy — he went into fits of

wild mad laughter and I joined him.

I made him promise not to tell anyone about the accident. My husband would have a fit and I would never be left clean a window again. He would never feel safe leaving me behind him. Paddy was not so sure. I could have met 'me end' he told me.

I brought him into the kitchen. He saw the table and it only gorgeous and all.

'Christ, if you was killed Missus,' he said, taking off his cap in respect — whether for me or my Maker I do not know — 'if you was killed and all that grandeur laid out for them, it would kill them! If my missus could cook like that,' he continued, 'God...'

I put the biggest creamiest flan in a box and handed it to him.

'Take that home for your tea, Paddy,' said I.

He got the message straight away.

'I never laid eyes on you today love,' says he, tipping his cap and just making it out the back door as my visitors streamed in the front.

The only ill effects I ever had from the fall is that my back felt queer for a few weeks. Then it gave me no more trouble again until the lump appeared, years and years later. With that creamy flan I bought the watchman's silence and I signed my death warrant.

The gas main was put down eventually. The trench was filled in. Then they put up the boundary fences. The day we had our back garden fully fenced, I nearly had a stroke. It seemed huge. It didn't shrink with age either I can tell you!

The front garden was pocket handkerchief size. It had a curving drive from gate to front door, on the plans. The kids have informed me, over the years, that one can get from gate to front door in thirty-four giant steps! The drive was covered with tarmacadam. The gardeny bit was a mass of rock formation. I spent days looking at it. Then the penny dropped. There was no earth. Not an ounce of soil, virgin or otherwise.

The builder explained the situation in full detail. They had removed a hill to straighten out the site for the estate.

We had no earth, — none of the neighbours had earth in their fronts, — and he had no earth to give us. Big deal.

My husband appealed to a builder clearing a site for a hotel. Please could we have it — some of it. No, was the answer. They could not shift earth out to us, we were too far — a mile to be exact. I got on the coat and away with me up on the bike. I told the builder my mother is from Cork — she is too — and I knew he was. A Corkman will do anything for another Corkman, I was told on good authority. To prove the point, he sent out some earth to our house, fourteen tons of it to be exact.

My husband arrived home from work that afternoon and could not get in the gate. Neither could any other man on the estate. You see the earth was free. The lorry driver deserved a tip, so I slipped him a half note. The other women on the estate saw ton after ton of beautiful brown earth cascading onto our drive. They came out in droves. Would he bring them some? I had a little chat with the driver. If they each gave him a half note, would he do it. Like hell, he would, he told me. They each got out their half note and they each got in their earth.

That night and the day after, we were all out shovelling. Every relation by blood or by marriage was called on to help. The skies darkened and the smell of rain haunted us all. If it rained we were ruined, the drives were ruined. We got to know the neighbours right fast. Every so often someone would drop out to take a rest, but all in all every one dug in literally. The earth got shifted at long last.

The relations and visitors disappeared and swore they would never visit the estate again. The father of the man across the road was inclined to get violent.

'What bloody lunatic's idea was it to bring all this bloody earth on to this bloody estate,' he shouted.

He crossed the road and spoke directly into my face 'If I had a hold of the bastard, I'd shoot him.' Having had his spake he went back to his shovelling quite happily. I was sweating from the work and him roaring was not helping to cool me, or the knowledge that I was the one due to get the bullet!

We flattened and destoned our beautiful earth.

Then we cut out flower beds. We also marked where the lawn would be when the seed was set and grown. The two of us went into Woolworths and bought a huge bag of plants in full bloom. A hand trowel each and an hour later we had an instant garden. Even without grass, it looked beautiful.

Now the flower beds are set in four layers. Springtime all the springtime flowers come up and come out. The daffodils, the crocuses, hyacinths, tulips and snowdrops leap annually out of the ground and die down again for another year. In the meantime all the summer flowers are on the way up and out: sleeping shamrock, phlox, sweetwilliam, marigolds; you name it, you will find it in that garden. The Michaelmas daisies and chrysanthemums follow on and remain with the roses up to Christmas most years. January, the snowdrops start the rush again. I never transplant or divide anything. They multiply away under the earth. Some people advise me to take up things and dust them down and put them away in bags to dry out for the winer. Nonsense, I tell them, I imagine it upsets the flowers' sex lives to disturb them, and I am rarely advised a second time by the same person!

Real toffee nosed ones look in over my wall at the masses of colour. One old moth one day had the audacity to say to me – ' One should not have a Madonna Lily so near a Red Hot poker – it is vulgar. '

Well, I ask you? You cannot please them all and anyway it is our garden. I would love to have a pennyworth of your one's garden. Madonna Lily – probably never grew one herself.

We grew fantastic sunflowers two years ago. Van Gogh would have adored them. These got huge altogether. I emptied the teapot on them twice daily. Then I had to stake them. Every headless brush handle was put into action. I designed cross shaped stakes to hold them. I had a bunch on each side of the front window. To see them tied to the stakes you would swear they were the two robbers cruxified with Christ. I mentioned this fantasy to my Mother and she nearly killed me. She said I was all kinds of a bad Catholic to even think such things. Still and she going off home that day she tiptoed past them with a frightened glance.

We grew monster hollyhocks another year and had to pin them onto the guttering. They had huge nodding heads. At night I used always close the drawing curtains and we in bed. They would be hitting the window on a windy night and you would imagine they were grinning at you in the morning. Especially if you had had a jar the night before.

I remember getting the lawnmower sharpened in a in a shop in town. It was to be sent out at the end of the week. I gave my address and the fellow gave me a very funny look.

'Are you living anywhere near the house with them terrible things growing up the wall?' he asked. 'The people that owns them must be mad,' he added.

'Just two doors up from that house,' I said without batting an eyelid.

As I went in our front garden coming in from town I looked at the hollyhocks. They seemed to be looking at me. In that split second I knew how Peter felt after disowning Jesus.

But back to the start of it all.

The outside was taking shape, in the front anyway. But the inside left a lot to be done. The windows—now we have only the usual three in front and three in the back, but you try making curtains for them for the first time and they look like millions.

I purchased miles of curtaining. I spent days measuring the windows. A few more days checking the measurements. Then I was off at a canter. Nothing ventured nothing won. I got out my best needle with the biggest eye and a few reels of thread and curtain after curtain was put up. The drapes, as my grandiose friends call them (drawing curtains to me and you) were fully lined. Miles and miles of net curtaining followed and the place looked real ducky. It did not deter me in the least that I had not a sewing machine. Lack of experience did not worry me in the least either. By the time those windows were covered I was ready to open a business as a fully trained curtain maker. My grandmother always used say that anyone can do anything if they try. I have proved time and time again that she was right!   You would see people going around moaning that they would love such a thing.... it is too dear or some other excuse.   These people wear me out.   If I cannot afford a thing, I try to make it myself.   If it is a success I show it to everyone.   If it is a failure I fire it into the bin and throw more dirt on top of it to hide it.   Then I go off and have a good cursing session with myself and get on with the next job!

In the height of gardening and home improvements, our first Christmas came on us.   I began to feel queerish. I put it down to overwork, excitement and overeating. In the January, I trecked into George for a tonic.   I got one all right!   I was going to have a baby, he told me. I was delighted and tore out of his surgery.   I jumped onto a bus going out my mother's way.   Unable to contain myself I grabbed the conductor by the arm.

' I am going to have a baby! ' I told the astonished young fellow.

He took me by the shoulders.   I was gently deposited in the cripple's seats.   You know the long ones just inside the door.

There were very few on the bus as it was mid-afternoon. One old man was reading a newspaper and two children were going home from music.

' You sit there quietly, ' says your man.   ' I'll get the driver to get you to a hospital. '

He gave a run up the bus like a streak of lightning.   If he did I gave a run after him like another streak of lightning. He clawed at the driver's communication window and I shook him by the coat.

' There is no hurry.   I - I have another six months to go, ' I told him.

He turned pale,and I assisted him back down the bus and the two of us sat side by side on the cripples' seat. ' God, Miss, ' said he,' you gave me a terrible fright. ' He was actually shaking.

' Isn't it great, ' I babbled,   ' I am having a baby. ' ' Look, Miss, ' he gasped, ' please don't start that again - I'm not able for shocks. '

By the time we got to my mother's stop I put him right as

to my married status.

All these years no matter where I meet him he gives a roar off the bus. ' How is the baby, Miss? '

Over the years he has got married himself. He has three little girls whose snaps I get shown if I get on his bus. The baby he thought I was having on his bus is now as tall as himself.

Having told my mother the good news, I proceeded back to wait for my husband to come from work. Then I told him. They got even more excited than the conductor. Later I went up to our smallest bedroom. It looked just right for my son's bedroom. Our house would be a home at least with the coming of our baby, I thought to myself.

CHAPTER
10

Spring has always been my favourite season. Maybe it is because I first met my husband in the spring. Ever since I watch the earth warming and the flowers coming up and the feeling of anticipation and promise is in the air. Always in the spring we plan our summer holidays, we plan to redecorate, to buy things, to go places. The children begin to take out marbles, rollar skates and skipping ropes. The sun shows up the dirt on the windows and on the furniture. Springcleaning gets under way. We go on day trips to the rivers or the lakes. As the days get warmer we get out the car-sickness tablets for the children and tear off to the seaside. This year I am only waiting for the Easter holidays to be off. The washing and cleaning can wait for the wet days. For us — this is going to be the best one. It may be the last. I refuse to think of next spring.

Oh, I have had wonderful springs, like our first 'married spring....'

The spring came, our first spring together. As well as my husband's fancy turning to thoughts of love, like all the other young men, he had to tackle the back garden. It was awful. No words, in English or any other language, could describe it, although I'll try, of course. It is painted on my brain in indelible colours. It was a big, wide, mass of dirt. There was clodded red clay for the first half. Then the garden went uphill. Then it flattened out into a kind of a road. Then thanks be to Almighty God it finished at the boundary fence. It was eighty feet long and forty feet wide. A bloody nightmare of a place.

My husband and I surveyed it with unbelieving eyes for ages. I was hoping that if we ignored it it might go away. But it didn't. Cats began to use it as a public convenience. They tore at the red clay making their commodes or whatever they think they are making. I used go mad. I would open the nearest window and throw the nearest thing at them. I began to get to be a fantastically good markswoman. The place was not enhanced with empty bean and pea cans and other miscellaneous missiles.

We then decided that if we were going to do it at all we would do it right. We got in a man with a rotavator. One look at our back garden and he went out faster than he came in. ' No rotavator would go on those rocks,' he told us as he left.

We got out two spades and a wheelbarrow and sallied forth against the elements. We were going to have a flat garden. The hill would be levelled and the red clay would be buried with the earth off said hill. This project kept us highly amused for quite a while. Sweat, blood, tears of temper and frustration wetted that hill. As a team we moved it. He had to do all the donkey-work of course. Due to my delicate condition, I was a bit curtailed. He swung the pick-axe with the wild abandon of one possessed. By the time we had it flat we discovered Nature had done a job on it. It had grown a crop of high, wild grass. We cut the garden in two, mentally for the moment. He continued fighting with the top bit. Day after day he would dig out a patch. By coincidence they seemed to measure 4' x 6'. I was afraid of my life to cross him for fear me and all belong to me would be buried in them. They multiplied and he got down to the invisable mark.

Running parallel with this excavation was another trench. This was for a path. This path was to have a foundation of small stones. For months we pegged every stone in sight into this open mouth.

Every morning I'd do a pilgrimage along this slippery, moving mound of loose stones. My clothes line was alongside it, you see. If I took off the shoes and stockings, said a few Hail Marys and had a few cups of black coffee, I was in business. I was convinced I was the only woman in the world to have a private Lough Derg just outside the kitchen door! Boy, did I do penance on that death trap. Each day I would set off with my little plastic bucket of clothes clutched to my bosom. My heart ticked painfully. I was armed with a pocketful of pegs and indigestion tablets clutched between my teeth. I battled bravely against wind, weather, the fright of slipping and fierce heartburn. I used make my way slowly and sorrowfully along. I used wonder would I break or burst some part of my anatomy before I would again reach the kitchen door. I simply adore drama and excitement, and those trips were the highlight of my pregnancy!

The grass seed got set in the top half, two flower beds were cut out and a huge section was marked off for a sun-trap of a patio. The overflow of stones from the path would act as foundation for this. The garden faces west and the whole place is a sun trap. The path trench was evened off ready for slabs of concrete. We were waiting for our son — the garden was waiting for slabs for the path, ready-mix concrete and the grass to grow. It seemed to me to have become pregnant in sympathy with me. Then a neighbour of my mother died. She left me fantastic bushes and we sadly filled the flower beds with them. We put down a white fence to cut off the no-man's land at the bottom of the garden.

On sunny days we would sit out in our two deck-chairs and survey our work. I would be busy with my knitting, in blue, of course. My bag was packed and I was mentally down on one knee for the word 'Go'. I moved from cloud nine onto cloud ten and then moved into the nursing home.

I went in on a Monday in high spirits. Five other girls in exactly the same condition moved in the same day. Their babies were born before nightfall. Tuesday, four more arrived and they had their babies before tea-time. Wednesday and Thursday, more mothers-to-be, were admitted, more new babies were born. Everyone seemed to have a baby but me. The priest attached to the home gave me a Maternity Blessing each day. Visitors arrived and left. George arrived and left. One nurse stayed with me all the time. Complication after complication set in. I will spare you the grim details, just give you the more dramatic highlights of the week.

On Friday, it was decided to shift me out of the nursing home and into one of the local hospitals. When the ambulance arrived it was decided I would not make the journey. They sent for the priest. I was passing in and out of a coma at this stage. In my lucid moments I heard George and another doctor discussing my condition with the nurses. Neither my baby nor I would survive the day. It was just one of those things and they seemed helpless. I was not in a very good condition to do anythir.g either. One of the nurses was upset as she was young and I was going to be her first patient to die. She had been very kind to me and I felt sorry for her. I felt very tired and would be quite content to fall asleep and jack it up altogether. Hazily, I thought of my husband and my mother and my sisters. I felt very sorry for them too. Then I thought of my baby, not yet born and, of my marriage. Our life together was only beginning. Were we not going to get any chance? Was our son never going to know the joy of living? Had my mother kept me alive in the boot box to go like this? Did my husband's love mean nothing to me? Did my child's life mean nothing to me?

These thoughts and many more passed through my mind. My body was worn out, the doctors and nurses were worn out. The priest gave me the last Sacraments. He blessed and prayed with me. He told me I would be happy with Jesus in heaven. I told him I was in heaven and he thought I was sinking faster than I should.

George and the other fellow came back. They shook their heads and gave me an injection. I refused to go to sleep, I was determined to have my baby. I was going home, but not the one they had in mind. Two hours later my son was born alive.

The baby was taken away and put down in the nursery with all the others. I was washed and cleaned up and laid out on the bed. I felt as if a hundred ton truck had driven over and back across my body since Monday! I was jaded tired. I was sore all over and felt I would never again rise out of the bed in this world. I seemed to melt into the mattress. My job was done so I fell asleep.

George arrived in again a few hours later.

'How the hell you didn't die I'll never know,' was his cheerful greeting. George is not a one for not putting a tooth in it, as my grandmother used to say.

'I just did not feel like it, that's why,' I retorted as I was getting back into my stride at that stage.

For a few days I was confined to bed. The baby was not brought near me. I was assured he was fine. Flimsey excuses were used for my not seeing him. One night I hid my usual sleeping pill and waited until three o'clock.

I crept downstairs and into the nursery. No one was there except the babies. I looked at them through the big glass window. There was about a dozen of them all asleep. They were like little sleeping cupids. I would have loved to cuddle each one to me. I then saw one little one. He was over in the corner. He had puffy eyes, he was all black and blue in the face and hands and looked for all the world like a battered boxer. I looked at the name on the moses basket. He was mine. Just then a nurse appeared. She assured me he was fine. The black and blue and puffy look would go. He had been marked by forceps and other instruments but the marks would go. I just stared at this little mite. 'Jesus,' I whispered to myself, 'Jesus how could you, how could you do this to my baby?'

I cried myself to sleep but I was grateful that he was alive. Ten days later the two of us went home.

My husband had the house full of flowers. I watched him as he gazed down on our son. All pain, sorrow and death seemed very far away. Hand-in-hand we tip-toed downstairs. The grass seed had come up in my absence. A smooth green carpet spread out before me. Birds sang in the trees beyond our boundary fence. I felt I was being given a second chance — oh, it was good to be young and it was even better to be alive!

During my waiting months I had read every book I think written about baby care. I am glad I did. Because to this day I have not time to read them. Our son turned out to be the hungriest child ever born. He roared for bottles non-stop. Especially at night. A good night's sleep was four hours. For the first twelve months I was like a lunatic. I used walk the pram into town every day to give him loads of air. Showing him off really. Well, I earned him didn't I? The nights were murder for us though. Up and down, pints and pints of milk: hot milk, lukewarm milk, anything. I suppose I was a very bad mother, maybe. Anyway the minute I would take my eyes off his he would yell to high heaven. I used try to hypnotise him to sleep. My husband used sing — on and on and on. To no avail, needless to say. Two weeks after his first birthday we packed a bag. We packed him off to my mother-in-law for two weeks. We left for London and left no forwarding address. We were going to get away for two whole weeks and no one could reach us. We were going to sleep.

We got to our hotel at three o'clock in the afternoon. We cancelled all meals until further notice. We put a 'Please do not Disturb' notice on our door and fell into bed.

We slept solid until 12 noon the following day. We landed down for breakfast as they were setting the tables for the next day's breakfast. The cook came out and told us to sit down. He gave us a full breakfast and wished us the very best of luck.

After breakfast we thanked them profusely. He asked us what we had intended doing for the afternoon. My husband said we intended going to bed. We woke the following day at about eleven o'clock. We had again missed breakfast. We tried to duck out of the hotel but the cook caught us. He again gave us a huge meal. We went out for a short walk and met him going off duty on our way back to the hotel.

'Bed,' he asked.

'Yes,' we gasped. The London air and the lack of disturbance in bed was really too much for us.

We finally succeeded in getting up in time to be last for breakfast. The cook took a great shine to us and always served us personally.

We went on tours of all the Museums and Galleries. We visited Buckingham Palace. I did not envy the queen her huge home — or her huge gardens. She was welcome to all the pagentry attached to her colourful life. All I would have liked was to take home one of her Nannys to mind my son!

Of course, we naturally missed Francis, our baby. We had called him after my husband. Every year old baby we saw we stared at. Our eyes would meet and we would each know what the other was thinking. 'Our baby is more beautiful!' Night after night we went to shows and to the theatre. We saw stars, who up to then were only names on paper.

We lapped up the sunshine in Trafalgar Square — I fell asleep there one afternoon. We had relations in Coventry and Cheshire but we did not visit them. We lazed around all day long. We were last out of bed every morning and could not wait to fall into it again at night. Sometimes we would return and take a little afternoon nap for good measure. We heard babies cry and we did not have to stir — it was really beautiful.

On the day we were leaving we said goodbye to our friend the cook.

'Had a good honeymoon?' he asked with a sly smile.

'We are not on our honeymoon,' I rushed to explain, 'we came here for a rest. We have a cross baby in Ireland and we came across the Irish Sea for a good sleep!' We shook hands, and bade him au revoir. I shall never forget his expression on his face; he looked disappointed!

We collected our son and heir and headed for home. Home now was shaping up nicely. We had plenty of painting done. Curtains screened us off from the outside world. When Francis was four months old, we had invested in our first car, a brand new one. We felt we were really progressing. We took him off to the seaside any fine week-end and he got a fabulous tan. Thinking again about that year of sleepless nights, I clean forgot about that wonderful car — I was like a miser clinging to all my new possessions. I had a husband, a son, a home and two gardens, plus the car, and more than anything else I had happiness. In this blase world it is asking for ridicule to admit one is happy in one's marriage. O.K. ridicule me.

CHAPTER

11

Pegging out the washing today I noticed primroses in the rockery. The last pair of knickers was put flying in the breeze and I took a seat on a large rock. I have always believed there to be great wisdom in the saying —

> ' What is this world if full of care
> We have not time to stand and stare.'

Each   19 April   we head out into the country to get primroses. It is Primrose Day. I take a little trowel and poke out a few plants for our garden. Mary gathers bunches which she presents to us on our return home. Then she makes a little altar with her statue of Our Lady. I often wonder will she have her children doing the same. Will my son drive his wife out the country to pick primroses? When my husband sees primroses in future springs will he remember...will he remember being young and in love? Will he remember breaking his comb and his penknife digging up primroses for me on the first month anniversary of our meeting? When he finds half his comb and a pressed primrose, will he be happy to know that I shall never forget — never in this life or in the next?

How could I forget in this life — our back garden is a living monument of our love.

After what I shall refer to as our second honeymoon we were full of beans. We were no sooner home and hardly unpacked than out the back door with the three of us. We had a lawn and the flower beds. We concreted the sun trap and we laid the flags or slabs on the path. Now do not ask me for any details of these projects. I was there, I was helping but, Glory be to God, I was falling asleep, I was amazed to see them, actually, when I looked at them after my two week rest.

We started digging the second half for another lawn. Then we decided to continue the path down the whole way and make another sun trap. At that stage nothing was too much for our agile bodies and agile brains. We tore at the mass of long grass down at the end. When we were tired we just laid down in it. I'm sure the neighbours thought we were having sexual relations but we weren't really. Anyway, we had Francis crawling around at that stage eating worms and earwigs. The added protein to his diet did not do him a bit of harm!

We pegged stones into the new trench for the path. This was not used as the clothes line only went as far as half-way in the garden.

At last we removed the trellis marking the middle of the garden. We set the lawn. We ordered more slabs for the path and we adjourned to the deck chairs because the long grass was gone. We adjourned quite often — well, Rome was not built in a day.

We laid the end bit to the long path making it full length and laid slabs in the new sun trap. This all sounds very easy on paper. One must remember that there was only two of us capable of work in our trio. We hodded, shoved, pulled and dragged those slabs into place. They are set at a slight slant so that they dry off fast after rain. God be with the youth of us. I would eat every one of them now I think before I could tackle that job again. We took odd looks at the mound of dirt. It grew a load of grass on it then. The grass grew up to about three feet high — like a huge head of green hair on a giant with a queer shaped head. It nearly drove us mad. I used to get nightmares from it.. Still I was grateful to sleep at any cost. All the air exercise and worms seemed to improve our son's sleeping habits. We used get an average of seven hours most nights.

We were doing fine. All we had left which was a bit queer looking was a heap of dirt at one side of the garden. This heap of dirt was forty feet long, about six feet wide and about three feet high. We ignored it for a while — a long while. Then my husband got a fantastic brainwave — we would have a forty foot long rockery. We got chemical weedkiller and killed all the growth. Then we discovered we had no rocks. We, who had been falling over rocks for the past few years. Where had they all gone! We broke them up with a pick-axe out of the ground and then smashed them with a sledge hammer. If ever either of us have to break stones in jail we will be experts.

My hand shook the cradle all night and most of the day broke rocks. Weaker sex, how are you!

We carried on regardless. We would have a rockless rockery. Then we discovered a site where there were large uneven lime stones. No one owned them — they had been dug up to build a wall. We drove over. I used to brush each stone, with a little yellow hearth brush, to remove any worms, slugs or such like crawlies. Away into the boot of the car and drive home with our precious bounty. They were so big we could only take two at a time. This site was beside the road. Passers-by used to slow down and gaze out at us. We must have looked like right lunatics. Me brushing the stones. We both risking hernias lifting them. Then driving away with two in the boot. A wonder we were not arrested! We have sixty rocks in that rockery and we earned every one of them.

We begged, borrowed, swapped and bought little plants for that rockery. Now it is a four season miracle.

While all this activity was going on our son was grwoing up by our side. We fed him, clothed him, loved him and played with him. The grandparents thought we were absolutely marvellous to produce such a wonderful specimen of humanity. We thought we were great too — probably helped to brainwash them, if it goes to that!

When he was in the pram everyone used to admire his blonde head of curls. My heart used swell with pride. When he started to walk he even looked more beautiful. I used wash, brush and comb his hair and it shone like spun gold.

My friends and contemporaries often warned me about the first hair cut. I could understand a child crying at the first visit to the barbers but the mothers crying too? I just could not understand it. In my own mind, with lack of understanding and from lack of experience, I thought it would have no effect on me. I'd march him into the barber's, get the job done, off we would go and get the messages, the usual cone each, and home. No bother, no fuss — and crying. I never cry unless I have good reason to and even then I'm not partial to floods.

The Grannys had being after me not to get it cut and I held out as long as I could so as not to hurt their feelings. People used take one look at his quite long curls and say, 'I thought you had a boy?' Francis used get very indignant at this insult to his manhood. I often caught him with a scissors barely in time.

One fine day we made off to the barber at last. This particular barber had cut his father's hair and his grandfather's hair before him. I was going to keep up the tradition.

Francis cried a little in the chair; the barber had a big job as he had lashings of curls. I had my shilling and sixpence ready for fear he would kick up ructions and we would have to make a quick exit. When he was finished, I handed the barber a pound note. While his back was turned getting the change, I was very busy. I gathered loads of the golden curls off the red and white tiles and stuffed them into my pocket. I took my change and my child and ran out of the shop.

My eyes were smarting and the tears tasted salty in my mouth. I could not cry in the street so I made for the nearest church. My little boy sat in a seat in front of me and I knelt on the last kneeler. I saw the little shorn head, just a crest of curls on top, and my heart nearly broke. Hot tears coursed swiftly and silently down my cheeks. There were no sobs, no sound, just the feeling of utter desolation.

A hand gently touched my shoulder. It was the gnarled hand of an old, old woman. She had a black shawl, going green with age, on her grey head. Two gentle, faded blue eyes gazed with sympathy out of a lined, care-worn face. She had a black jumper and skirt, a blue patched pinafore and broken boots on her otherwise bare feet.

'Are you sick, love?' she asked gently. Silently I shook my head.

'Did you lose someone, love, someone died belonging to you?' she questioned softly.

'I've lost my little baby,' I blurted out through the tears, 'my baby is gone. He is a little boy now.'

I pointed to my son who was now running a red fire engine along the seat.

He was oblivious of the drama that was going on behind him and just as well too.

The old woman knelt beside me.

'I know how you feel love,' she whispered to me, 'I've reared

seven boys you see. Only a mother knows the taste of salty tears. The first hair cut, the first day at school, they go to work, maybe across the sea and get married. You keep breaking your heart from the minute they are born — you never loose them though — you will always be their mother.'
I dried my tears and the three of us genuflected and went into the sunshine. She shook hands with Francis and ambled off. Her back was bent from age and the hardships of life. I felt very humble that this lovely old lady could console me. Looking at her broken boots I felt I should be consoling her. I thought I had everything. She knew she too had everything; was she too not a mother?
I tightened my grip on my little boy's hand and off we went. 'Look what I have,' he piped up. Looking down I saw a penny in his hand.
'Where did you get that?' I asked, thinking he had picked it up in the Church.
'Holy God's Mammy gave it to me,' he said, 'remember you were talking to her — the lady in the black cloak.'
Even in her poverty the old woman had parted with a penny.

I have never seen her again but I am grateful for her help over my first milestone as a mother.

Tucked away, among old letters from my husband, I have a little blue envelope. In it are the golden curls I picked off the floor of that barber's shop. In tissue paper also in the envelope is the penny. I swopped it for one of my own that day, now so long ago. Francis' young bride might like to have those momentos of his childhood. I should like them to pass onto the next generation. When his wife romances around some town, some day, with his baby in a pram she can remember me. No matter what mistakes she will make — I have made worse ones. No matter how she dotes on him — it will be only history repeating itself — a pity that it is destined that we shall not meet.

At the moment I have not time to take the luxury of being sorry for myself.

CHAPTER

12

Somebody once said 'When you are a child you think like a child and when you are a man you think like a man.' I think that is a great note, as Tits Murphy would say. But I think that it would be better if a man was capable of thinking like a child and a man when he had reached his years of manhood. That is what I would wish for my son anyway. I would hate to think of him with all grown-up ideas and sophistication. My prayer for him is that he will retain the innocence of childhood under the veneer of manliness. I should hate him to loose the childish fascination towards the world. The ability to question God and man and the ability to have his own answers to these questions, be they right or wrong. God, will I ever forget the questions he asked me in his youth. Non-stop all our waking hours. I think the best one I was ever asked is 'What is the stars?'

'What is the stars?' How many times has that question being asked in many theatres in Sean O'Casey's immortal play *Juno and the Paycock?* I will never forget one night, shortly after *the* haircut, I was putting our little boy to bed. I stood spellbound and watched him. He stood, in muted light, hands clasped, and asked me that same question. He had the nonchalant stance of MacLiamoir and the timidity of a beginner. Did I fancy I was the mother of a budding actor. God give you sense, I was too busy racking my brain as to how I would answer that six marker.

'Now love,' I told him gently, so as not to overexcite him, and have him awake all night, 'they are all little angels going to bed; the stars are the lights on their candles.'

I kissed him and tucked him in and told myself I was rearing him lovely.

I was no sooner out on the landing than he called me. 'Come here Mammy,' he shouted at me. In I went and saw that he was sitting bolt upright in the bed.

'Do you see those stars?' he asked me.

'Of course I see them,' I answered.

'They are the lights at the end of the angels cigarettes, that

74

is what they are.' With that gem of information he turned in for the night.

I made my way slowly downstairs. 'Jesus,' I prayed to myself, 'that is the modern child for you now.'

Secretly the idea rather appealed to me; I imagined the archangels fogging away at the King Size varieties and the lesser angels puffing at the cheaper smellier ones.

When we got what was his first fall of snow he was absolutely estatic. All tools were downed that morning. I closed the kitchen door on the breakfast ware and it unwashed; the beds were not made, nothing had seen a sign of a duster. Away out with us into the back garden. We made a father and mother of a snowman. He was complete with eyes, nose, hat and scarf. I hadn't made a snowman for years and was having a whale of a time. We made snowballs and pelted each other and the snowman. I saw an odd neighbour glance out her window as she did her beds like a dutiful housewife. The two of us rolled and shouted like two children in the snow.

Coming on to dinner hour we adjourned to the kitchen — someone had to cook a dinner!

We stared out in wonder at the snow laden trees. We admired our beautiful snowman. He was not exactly an architectural triumph but he was smashing all the same.

'Do you know what snow is?' my son asked me tentatively. 'Well,' I said as I tried to think up a nice educational answer. 'It is cotton wool,' he continued, as if I had never spoken, 'cotton wool out of the angels tablets' bottles.'

I looked at him in amazement. What kind of a rearing was I giving him?

There he stood before me an innocent child. He really believed that the Heaven was full of chain-smoking, drug addicts of Angels. Did I try to persuade him to think differently? Not on your life. I let him off. Sure don't I have queer ideas about heaven myself at times.

While my dinner was bubbling away I thought about heaven. Different people have different ideas of it you know. Priests and nuns and books will give you their angle on it. I had an uncle once and he told me that his idea of being in heaven was very simple. He would love loads of porter and a red-head sitting on each side of him. Tits Murphy told me her idea of heaven was to have the Garden of Eden all to herself and her second husband. His name was Joe. She had not him buried at all. She kept him in the house all her life — he was cremated in England and she had him in a jar.

When Tits died she left me Joe's remains. We have him in our dining room. We are quite used to him actually. The children often give the container a shake to hear the rattle of the ashes. I used shake the devil out of him when I was a child. Tits put sticky tape around the cover so there is no fear of him spilling out on top of us.

I know quite a few people who have lifted up his container to admire it. These same people, if they knew its contents, would die on the spot. God forgive me, I laugh away inside myself, I feel sorely tempted to tell them it's secret. But, knowing better, I refrain.

During those halcyon days of Francis' childhood, I again learned to look at the world through the eyes of a child. While his father was at work we used walk hand-in-hand. As his father helped me look at the world through an adult's eyes, here I was having anot... peep at it through the eyes of his son. For him there were no grey skies I was to learn.

One of the dirtiest, filthiest, blackest looking days I remember looking out the dining room window. A dark grey sky hung overhead, clouds raced along ready to drop snow or sleet down on top of us. The grass was real tatty looking. The clothes on the line looked as if they would never dry again in this world. The flowers were crystalised from the frost. Everything was rotten — I wondered would the winter ever go away. I then heard a shout from my son.
'Look out there,' he yelled, 'look at the sky, look what is happening.' I looked — it was the same dirty grey as it was a minute ago.
'It is a filthy dirty sky,' I said to him with the irritation creeping into my voice.
He shook me by the arm. 'Look,' he shouted, 'God's mother is burning the dinner — look at the smoke coming out of her pots.'
I hugged him to me and prayed to God that all his life he

will look at the world, not with the jaundiced look of an adult, but the keen eyes of a child.

While the world was doing its level best to grind itself to a stop, me and my son were stopping and staring, so to speak. He was discovering the world for the first time and I was discovering it for a second time. I am afraid, when he is older, he will not remember me as a topper of a house cleaner or the like. He will remember me as a companion, an expert toy mender and ball player. Not to mention snowman maker!

Did I spend those few precious years of his childhood solely with him? God, I didn't. He had two Grannies and they were first class baby-sitters. In the evenings his father and I would go out — as often as financially possible. We still do. We would go to a picture or a dance or any dog fight that was going on.

During our son's second summer we went off on our third honeymoon. We left him in my mother's capable hands. This time we left our address! Not that she bothered writing to us. She was in her seventh heaven — to her he was the son she never had. She spoiled him to the last. He was allowed take his tricycle all around her house. In my day I would have been murdered if I even thought of bringing mine inside the back door. He is my father and mother-in law's first grandchild — over the years my brothers-in-law and sister-in-law have got married. They too have produced grandchildren for their parents. But our son is the eldest and if there is any question of babysitters, I casually drop in the fact that he was not exactly easy to have. Not blackmail — just a reminder of my darkest hours, anyway, I love getting out!

CHAPTER

13

These days I stand by and watch the young mothers of our estate getting their toddlers ready for walks. These toddlers mushroom up and are ready for school in what feels like mere months. I often feel like saying to these young mothers, 'God, enjoy these fleeting years — they will never come back.' It is at times like this that I thank God most profoundly that I am a mother. I also thank Him for giving me the time to enjoy my children's childhood. I have got so much and I feel that I have nothing to give back in return. Young Francis grew fast from being a wakeful baby to being a terribly lovable little boy.

Life continued at a steady trot for the three of us. We went on week-end picnics to the seaside. When Francis saw the rough sea for the first time after he had learned to talk, he was thrilled. The promenade was lined with people sitting in the sun. We landed, as usual, like a summertime Flight into Egypt. Bags of spare clothes, food and various sand buckets, balls and deck chairs. Everyone was at their dead ease staring into space, in a semi-coma from the heat. All of a sudden your man spotted the sea.

'O, my God,' he shouted with perfect diction, 'my God, look at the big bath.'

Heads turned, eyes opened and half clad bodies shook with laughter. What could we do but join them in their mirth.

Summer ran into summer, it seemed in those days. Then the year came when he was four. All his pals on the road of the same age were preparing for school. The mothers seemed to be overjoyed at the prospect, although I tried to persuade a few reluctant ones to hold out for another year. The little fellows seemed so small. In the end birth certificates were handed in and names were taken.

The week before the school opened the three of us went to town to buy his uniform. Short grey pants, pale blue shirt, royal blue tie, three-quarter grey socks, black shoes. I withered an old man who tried to sell me cheap shirts.

I insisted on the dearest — I wanted him to be like a prince. If he was going — he was bloody well going in great style!

The night before school opened I gave him a fine bath. I scrubbed his hair. The minute he was in bed I ran around the neighbourhood. Any reprieve, anyone backing down? I was met with determined faces — and a few ready-to-fill eyes. They were definitely all going. If I kept him at home he would be a year behind all his little pals. He might feel inferior in later years. No — he too would have to go.

Next morning his father and myself jerked in and out of sleep from five o'clock onwards. At eight-thirty I dressed Francis. I had to turn away as his Dad tied his dark blue tie. His very first tie. Then my masterpiece of a jersey went on — there was not a fault in it, honestly.

We went into the school, leaving my husband at the gate. The yard was full of mothers and children. Some crying, some coaxing. We carried on passed them and a nun showed us his new classroom. There were rows of little boys, red-eyed and tearful. Their nun took Francis by the hand and I turned and walked away. I met girls I was in school with in my youth, who had left in children for the first time too. No one saluted; no one spoke. If anyone had spoken to me, I would have roared crying into her face.

I met my husband at the gate and summoned up a watery smile. 'You'd be proud of him,' I chatted, 'he went in without crying or anything.' He had not to go to work until after dinner. We had a full morning ahead of us. Empty and lonesome. We drove off, past our own house, and away into the country. I glanced at my husband's averted face.

'We'll take a spin — the house would be very silent,' he commented quietly. He felt it too and I was glad I had not to face the emptiness so soon.

Having prepared dinner and shoving it in the oven to keep warm we went down to collect our hero. There were about thirty four-year-olds lined up for collection.

There they stood, all dressed the same. The very best of trousers and shirts. Knotted ties now slightly crooked. The navy jerseys — slightly too big — knitted with more love than talent.

With a feeling of surprise and awe, I realised every

mother had felt exactly like me. Nothing but the best for her son. Believe it or not I could not pick out our son. Then I saw him. I chided myself. How could I miss his blonde head and those big blue eyes. Then he spotted me. He threw himself into my arms. Other mothers spotted their precious sons. We took them by the hand and proudly walked out the gate.

We merrily greeted each other, 'See you in the morning — we shall spend all our time on the road, from now on.'

I spent very happy times in the school shed swapping yarns with the other mothers. Some of them were old friends, some were new. We had a little social club atmosphere about us. Shrieks of wild laughter were not uncommon to be heard renting the air. The stories we swapped were only priceless. The scandal we swopped — Boy! One could write a book on it alone. Make a fortune too because it would be banned straight away. The minute the bell would go and the children start to rush out one could feel the change. No longer were we scandal mongers and story tellers; we were mothers. A passer-by would see us coming out those gates, models of modern motherhood. Mothers to be proud of. Architects of the minds of the men of tomorrow.

CHAPTER

14

I spent an hour today consoling a neighbour who is expecting next August. Glory be to God, I thought I would never see the day when a one would come to me for consolation. She wouldn't mind, she told me, but she is on The Pill. There was no mention of The Pill when I was first married. With all the modern methods of birth control now, am I destined to have no grandchildren? I hope that if my children marry they will know the joy of being parents. I would hate them to miss out on the pleasures we have had in rearing them. Certainly they will have plenty of worries, just like we have had, but given my time again I would not change one moment of my motherhood.

After Francis was born I was told that it was medically impossible to have another child. I took the news calmly. After all I had him and felt lucky to have him. I would be quite happy to rear him and knit him into my life. He was very lively company and his pals were numerous. He was not spoiled — well, not too much anyway. Another child was not really necessary to keep him in his place. But, in my innermost heart, I longed for a little girl. I rather fancied dressing her up and curling her hair. I would buy all kinds of ribbons and frilly frocks for her. I could make clothes for her dolls. I could make dolls for her. With a boy — well, a trousers and shirt and he is dressed. A few toy cars and soldiers, a bike and he is off.

When Francis started school I tore around, as usual, like a lunatic, doing my housework, and visiting my mother and my in-laws as usual. Our social life continued to be as full as we could manage to pack it. I cycled in and out to the school to collect His Nibs. But I got notions, like my grandmother's best broody hen. Time was that I would like my daughter.

I began to feel queer — I hugged the secret to myself. I would tell no one for a while — just in case. Quietly and secretly I began knitting little garments, in pink of course, hiding them in the bottom drawer of my dressing table.

Then I decided to see George. I was mad to hear his verdict and I nearly went mad when I did. I was not four months pregnant; I had bloody anaemia. He gave me tablets to make me feel better, iron tablets. I could have screamed. When I got home there was a telegram from one of my sisters. She had had a daughter that morning. I tearfully wrapped up all my little knitted things in tissue paper. Tiny pink pom-poms — tiny pink bows. I sent them off to her. A week later I held her baby girl in my arms, I was her Godmother. My heart felt very heavy. I counted my blessings mentally. I had my husband, his son, our lovely home — no, nothing would console me. I would love to have a daughter.

The following year the three of us toured nearly three quarters of Ireland. From home to Dublin, Cork, Waterford and back. Even the animals in the zoo had loads of daughters!

Another school year started. I began to feel queer again. Not this time, I would not fool myself this trip. I went off to the chemist and got a bottle of a hundred iron tablets. I ate them, over a period of time, of course. I purchased another hundred. They were devoured according to my physician's instructions of last year. I purchased another bottle. At this stage I felt as if my guts were re-inforced with iron. My husband got nervous seeing me, becoming what looked like a drug addict. He advised me to see George.

I went into George and told him the bloody tablets he recommended me were useless. I had anaemia badly. I had eaten two hundred and seventy iron tablets over the past few months and there was not a drop of blood in my body. 'Did it ever dawn on you, you could be pregnant?' was his dry comment.

'I am not medically capable of becoming pregnant again,' I told him or according to you anyway, I added.

He did various tests. He checked and double checked. Then he told me the news. I was five months pregnant.

I didn't believe him. I thought he was playing a cruel joke on me. I was in no humour for jokes like that. I ate him. He was not a bit put out and he ate me back.

The following week was my husband's birthday. I got a great

plan I would keep the news till then.

In that week I floated around the place. Everyone commented on my good looks. I was placid, I was happy, I was in a semi-trance. I do not know how many times I nearly blurted it out to my mother. But I held out.

On my husband's birthday I sent him the usual card but I also sent him another one.

'Congratulations on your new Baby' was written on it.

He handed it back and said, 'You sent me the wrong card love.'

'No, I did not,' I said, 'you are going to have a daughter in four months time.'

He thought I was joking. So did my mother and his mother. I couldn't wait to get to town to buy a maternity dress. I was like a stick inside in it so I left it in the shop. I got loads of pink wool and started knitting as fast as I could. I gathered all the usual paraphernalia into a suitcase and carried on tearing around as usual.

Then one night we made a mad dash across the town at three in the morning to the nursing home. The next day Francis junior was installed at my mother's and Francis senior went back to his mother's.

All the next day I was still hanging around in the nursing home. A priest, a stranger, gave me a Maternity Blessing.

Is this the same as the last time?' I asked George. He only shrugged his shoulders.

My husband came and I could tell by the set of his face he was worried.

We were back to square one. All the terror of the last confinement came back to me. I wanted to go home. I did not want to have to go through the same thing again. Maybe this time I would not come out so handy.

But, I did. In the middle of the night our little daughter was born. The nurses had left me on my own as I seemed fine. I left them off somehow, I knew things would be all right. When I rang my bell, my nurse came. She thought I was joking when I told her my baby had been born. George was sent for but all he had to do was congratulate me.

Young Francis was mad for a sister from the time he

was about three years of age. He used look into each passing pram and ask why he had no sister. When I knew I was definitely expecting again I asked him would he like a brother, the answer was a definite no. If I had had another boy I do not know what I would have done.

Word was sent, hot foot, to my mother and to Francis junior. They were thrilled with the good news.

The day Francis was born he nearly caused my death. The day his sister was born he nearly caused the death of quite a few of my mother's neighbours. Now my mother lives on an avenue where lots of Grannies and Grandas live, and they all knew I was in the nursing home and were waiting for the good news. The day our little girl was born Francis was sitting on my mother's front step. The old woman, living two doors up, came down the avenue and asked him how was his mother.

'My Mammy is gone to heaven,' he told her, 'to get me little sister.'

The unfortunate woman took the worst meaning out of that gem of information. Knowing how bad I had been when I had him she thought that this time I definitely had died. In she went to my mother.

'God, Susan,' said she to my mother, 'I heard about Ellen.'

'Yes,' said my mother who had not yet fully recovered her full flow of speech.

'What will you do about young Francis?' asked her friend.

'Oh, I'll keep him for the time being,' answered my mother, 'that was what she wanted'

The old lady patted my mother's arm, ran out with tears rolling down her cheeks and she circled the neighbourhood spreading the news.

My mother was up to her elbows in flour and the radio blaring and the door bell rang again. Out she went and, according to her, about a million people were outside the door. She thought it was an election or something. Then they all started shaking her hand and telling her how sorry they were for her loss.

She, of course, thought they had fresher news than her. They had to put her in her shock chair and get her water. Luckily my husband appeared just then, fresh from the nursing home. He broke the news to all the neighbours and they were relieved, to say the least of it. A week later I was back in circulation once more. I had to listen to everyone's side of the story. It was lovely to feel genuinely loved by these old folk. I left my little baby behind for two weeks. She had been small and I wanted to get Francis used to the idea of having her before I actually produced her. He nearly went mad when I arrived home without her.

I shall always remember the day we brought her home. The house seemed to be full of flowers. The gardens were really at their best. I had the house shining. A huge line of colourful washing was soaking in the sun. Birds sang in the nearby trees. All I needed was a chorus in the background singing 'This is My Lovely Day' like you would see in old movies!

I carried her in along the shining tiles in the hall. I laid her carefully on one of the chairs in the dining room. Her black hair was close to her head like a wet-look swimming cap. Her eyes were two pools of navy blue. She looked me straight in the eye. She had the look of innocence of a baby but also the uncanny look of knowledge of an old, old woman. Her skin was olive colour, completely flawless. She was small and short and just like a real cuddily doll. As I looked at her, spellbound, her eyes began to close. She gave a real, tiny, ladylike yawn and fell fast asleep. Her tiny hands were gracefully laid out beside her and her lovely little feet peeped out from under the pastel coloured rug that covered her.

Young Francis was the first to break the silence.

'Can she really stay with us forever?' he asked.

'Yes, love,' answered his father as he too stood looking down at this little baby doll.

'She is terribly beautiful,' he said as he looked from her to me.

'Yes, love, she is,' I replied.

I stood looking at him as he gazed at his daughter. Young Francis also gazed at her in wonder. No one said a word — no one noticed me moving away. I felt a tug at my heart. There was a lump in my throat and I felt kind of weak. I walked unsteadily into the kitchen.

'I'll get the tea, lads,' I called brightly, no one was listening. My reign in an all male establishment was over. I used to be the only female in their lives. In there in the dining room lay my dream come true. A beautiful, perfect daughter. Here was I being really stupid because the two men in my life had deserted me. I got out the frying-pan and lashed on the eggs and rashers and told myself to have more sense.

The days, the months — yes, the years that followed that day have been wonderful. She was christened Mary — I had thought up real exotic names but I got murdered on all sides. My mother knew a one at school, a real fat one called Yvonne, my mother-in-law knew someone else whom she didn't like called something else. I daren't call her after one of them. I daren't call her after either Granny either — or any of the numerous aunts. We at last decided on just Mary.

From the word go she was a model baby. She woke to the minute every four hours, took her feed, was winded, changed and fell asleep. No wakeful nights — nothing. I often put a looking glass to her mouth to prove to myself she was not dead. After the torture of broken nights with Francis I could not believe that she could be so good.

She learned to walk and to talk and wrapped herself tighter and tighter around our hearts. On sunny days she would disappear down the garden with her brother where they would spend hours whispering on the garden seat. When the key would go in the front door you would hear the skidder of her feet. Her Dad was home. Her baby voice would babble away as she told him all the wonders of her day. The joy in her face as she looked at him was lovely to watch. He may have only gone to the bank down the road, to her he could be back from outer space, her welcome was so great. Even in the passing years, the world has never ceased to be a complete playground to her and a place of never ceasing wonder. While Francis was at school and his father at work, we girls went for walks. Again I could see the world through the eyes of a child. We would admire the fragile legs of a daddylonglegs, the colours on a wasp's back, the colours of a butterfly's wings. Budding branches were again pointed to me, seedlings breaking the earth, growing into flowers and blossoming, miracles before our very eyes. Her first steps, her first words, her first snowfall. History again was repeating itself. For her first snowfall we made not alone the father and mother of a snowman but the grandmother and grandfather of one. We had the help of her big brother. He was the hugest snowman in the world, at least, that is what they told me. Tears fell as he melted away. I promised the snow would fall again another year. It did — it varied each year. It was only this year we had enough snow to really let ourselves go. The snowman this year was six foot high. One or two years they were only leprechaun sized fellows, but, nevertheless, they were snowmen.

Her first four years slipped by like a beautiful dream. The day had to be faced again when I had to take a child to school for the first time. Her uniform was purchased: blue pinafore frock, grey jersey and blue cardigan, white socks and brown shoes. God how my heart broke as I watched her face into school for the first time. She was not a bit perturbed though. She sailed in and sailed out again at lunch hour.

'Thanks be to God,' said she with a backward glance, 'I do not have to go for another day.'

That is always her attitude to life. If she has to do something, well she gets on with it and then it is done. She has faced the dentist with the same outlook. There is no diddering around — do it and forget it.

She settled down in school and was very happy. She was only there a few months when a dog attacked her. He jumped at her face one day. Luckily I threw my hand out between them. His teeth sank into my right hand. As if in a nightmare I removed his teeth from my hand. She was unharmed — except for a fierce fright. We went home and surveyed the damage.

I put about six pillowslips around my hand and got on with the fish and chips for the dinner. After dinner I asked my husband to drive me to the hospital. He had no notion of how bad the hand was. I was met by a black doctor who nearly devoured me for not going down sooner. The hand was in mush. I got eight stitches and a terrible telling off. The guards were notified and called for statements. I described the dog — I'll never forget him.

With all the running here and there with the Guards to look for the dog, and housework and gardening, the stitches all burst! I went down again to the Accident Department and got eight more stitches. These rotted as the hand knitted and all I have is a scar. I always thank God, that it is not on my daughter's face.

When she was six years old I got an electric sewing machine and taught myself dressmaking. I made her six dresses for that summer and they were a terrific success. I told all my friends, of course. I did not tell them of all the tears of temper and frustration that went into my lessons. I made a few dresses for myself and a summer trouser-suit. Home dressmaking is the cheapest way of having a bulging wardrobe for next to nothing.

That sewing machine really went to my head. I got miles of material and covered my famous eiderdown. I made new curtains to replace the handmade ones. They had worn to threads over the years. The sun had them faded to nothing. I did not dump them in the dustbin or anything. Model wife that I am I made quilts of them. Covered old blankets with them I did. Turning the curtains inside out first — I'll have you know. Absolutely no money would pay me! A model wife and mother.

Then it came up to Mary's First Communion. I designed her outfit. Sleeveless dress of embroiderie anglaise with a coat over it of the same material. Trimmed with embroiderie anglaise. The same thing would have cost about £26 in the shops. I made it for just under £5. It was really fabulous. I had to wash the outfit — it had got grubby from handling it. I put it on the line, took it in, ironed it. I then put it out to air it. A bird went to the toilet on it. Back to square one. I will leave my language to your imagination!

Wash, iron, air, it was perfect. Tried it on for a dress rehearsal. I put on the beautiful white veil and the socks and shoes. She looked exquisite. Then her nose started to pump — the blood fell down the white outfit before my very eyes. I was completely immobilised by sheer shock. When I did get moving the dress and coat were soaked with blood

I gently removed them and consoled her. I soaked them in water and washed them once more. I got the impression that the outfit would never make the altar rails on The Day. But everything turned out perfect. She looked absolutely beautiful. All her class were all dressed in white too. They sang the Mass and tears fell into my prayerbook as I listened to them.

Francis had made his First Communion some years earlier. He was all glamour too in his first real suit. His first day at school feeling engulfed me as I saw him march out of the house for his Sacrament. After the breakfast he went off out playing with his filthy football under his arm. It was the first time that morning I relaxed. He was himself, clutching that football. She insisted in staying in her clothes all day and each fine Sunday after. She adored her glamorous outfit.

Year by year, she has grown more beautiful. She has been a wonderful addition to our lives. Just to see her sunny smile each morning makes it easier to greet the new day. I always thank God for her. She may have stolen my place in my husband's and my son's hearts — this other woman I have produced — but she has also stolen my heart.

CHAPTER

15

Today is just one of those days. The vacuum cleaner just packed itself in half-way around the floor. The washing machine started going a hundred miles a minute and that had to be stopped. Then this bloody big dog started tearing up my lilies. I let fly at him with the sweeping brush and the head fell off the brush. Suddenly I felt helpless without all my mod. cons. I hadn't them when I started my life on t.. ad of married bliss. God, I thought to myself, those were the days.

Before I got married I had visions of myself as a housewife. I really fancied myself. I would have a beautifully furnished home and I would be dancing around the place with a coloured feathery mop. In the future — near future — I could hear the patter of little feet. I would be producing meals in front of the man of my life. They would be like the pictures in coloured cookery book photographs. Everything would be ever so easy. Everything would be ever so clean and shining and I would look like a film star. In the evening we would sit hand-in-hand in the twinkling firelight listening to the radio, television not being heard of in Eire at the time. He — the man of my life — would only have eyes for me and we would spend our days and our nights whispering sweet nothings to each other.

Well, Jesus gave me sense. He went a very peculiar way about it but eventually I did get His message!

After a few weeks of marriage I found out I was not half as efficient as I thought I was. Neither was I half the bloody good cook I thought I was. I could do the cooking bit all right — it was the timing. Dinners on the table at one sharp. Breakfasts at eight sharp and things like that. Things got dirty faster than I thought. The patter of little feet is a myth. A herd of healthy elephants could make less noise than a healthy two-year-old running around over your head.

I was useless at lighting a fire. I would get the usual paper, sticks, fire-lighters, coal and a box of matches. A monster size box of matches. Then a bellows. Then a newspaper tucked around the fire place. This would always go roaring up the chimney like a bloody bull. I would throw in a cup of parafin oil — salt — sugar — even dripping out of my chip pan. God, how I used to curse. The tinker's litany would be repeated over and over again in beautifully modulated tones. These tones would rise to a dangerous height as the charred remains of the paper, etc., refused to redden. I used to persuade myself I was born for better things. I should have staff. Where the hell were all the Sugar Daddies? Where the hell were the matches? I would call on my Maker for help. I would ask His Mother to help me. For just the fire to fly up the chimney like everyone else's, just for once, I would have gladly sold my soul, or even my body. Often we were expecting visitors and the fire refused to blaze. When eventually it did catch and they arrived I would be smiling. That smile covered a real black mind. I could have cheerfully killed the whole lot of them. The Boston Strangler was only a beginner, an amateur; I could have strangled him as well as the visitors, all over the fires.

The continuous race against dust, dirt, cobwebs, lighting windows and non-lighting fires. I really needed a method. I set out the jobs to be done. I was really making a mountain out of a molehill. Every other young one on the road was flying around the place — why not me? Why not indeed. Young Francis arrived and threw out my timetable, what I had of one anyway.

One day when he was about three, I remember doing a bit of spring cleaning. I had the whole place up in a fierce mess. Furniture was scattered to the four winds: mats, rugs, chairs — the lot were out in the back garden. I had done a few hours scrubbing and polishing and the door bell rang. I went out, in filthy condition. A dirty apron adorned my dirty dress, torn stockings were up over my filthy knees. (Tights were not 'in' yet at the time). My face was probably filthy too. Outside the door stood a one of about sixteen. When she saw the condition of me she smiled broadly.

'Hi, love', says your one.

'Hi,' I gasped.

'Jesus,' said she, 'you are overdoing it aren't you.'

'Yes,' I answered, 'I am trying to do a bit of spring cleaning.'
'All the joints are lighting this time of the year,' she said as she ran her finger up my front door jamb (needless to say it was covered with dust).
'I am looking for a job,' she continued, 'just to save for my fare to England, seems you got here before me!'
'I did,' I said — I am not much good at conversation when I have been exerting myself. What with the lung, you see, I get breathless. She was going to do all the talking anyway, or so it seemed.
'You do not look as if you are paid much,' she commented, taking in the cut of the stockings and the rest of my ensemble.
'Bad enough,' I replied.
'That's the Irish for you. I'm looking for ten bob per hou and my card stamped,' she told me confidentially. 'Som bosses would expect you to go to bed with them and all. could tell you a few stories about some fellows I have worke with, in this town too. Real snobs on the outside, bloody rape you as soon as they would look at you. I could tell you all about them, I could,' she threatened.
I was hoping to God that she would. I was mad for a bit of entertainment as well as a bit of scandal. To my utter disappointment she refrained on filling me in on the details.
'Best thing you could do,' she confided in me, 'get the bloody boat for England — jack it up here — you will never get nowhere here.'
Then she pierced the knife deeper into my pride.
'You best clear out of here,' she waved at my filthy semi-detached, 'you are not getting any younger, you aren't.'
That nearly finished me. At the time there must have been only a few years between us.
After a few more sentences she bade me farewell. I watched her walk out the garden and out the gate. With a cheery wave she was gone.
I ran into the kitchen and looked in the mirror. Jesus, such a face looked back at me: hair scraped back, a white face with black circled eyes. A bloody panda would have looked better. My clothes were a disgrace. I was a disgrace. How could anyone so dirty run a dirty house.

I rushed and cleaned the place. I then stripped myself down to the skin. I had a bath. I washed my hair. I washed my clothes. I was turning over a new leaf. Somehow I would have to have a timetable. Otherwise I would be a dirty housekeeper in a dirty house and have dirty children into the bargain.

God, the humility of being taken for your own maid. 'What is the world coming to' I asked myself. I took another look in the mirror and was not greatly impressed with what I saw. At least the mirror was cleaner and so was I. That was a start I supposed.

I had a seven-room house and a seven-day week. What could be simpler I thought to myself. A room per day as well as the usual meals, beds and that kind of stuff. I kept that up for ages — until the novelty had well worn off it. I used have to double up on the rooms some days. It ended up that one day a week I was doing the house from top to bottom. Weeks came when something else cropped up and the days flew. Needless to say the dust did not fly. It settled down on everything and I was back at square one.

Then I decided to do the upstairs one day and the downstairs another day. It was which day though! I would get one half done. Then the sun would shine and I would lay my workworn and weary body down in the garden and soak up Vitamin C. Instead of taking half my house assunder and cleaning it and the rain lashing out of the Heavens I would sit down and read! I might even do some knitting — or sewing.

If the dinner was late, I had methods for playing for time. I would meet my husband, in the hall, with a genuine amorous embrace. This would lead to maybe a little court. The dinner would be boiling, stewing or roasting away nicely while we enjoyed part of his dinner hour.

If I thought I was overdoing the loving wife bit too many days in a row, I had to change my tactics. A bush carefully dug up and placed on the door-step never failed to stop him in his tracks. God forgive me, on the two occasions I used that time consuming ruse, I blamed the tinkers!

I could always start a slight argument to kill a few

minutes. A genuine sounding story about a man ringing at the doorbell. I couldn't answer because I was in the bath or even on the toilet. I saw the figure all right at the door but couldn't get down. Someone very important I was quite sure — could be one of his brothers I would say at a random guess. By the time we had conjectured who the caller could have been — sure wasn't I putting a fine, well-cooked meal before him, — all thoughts of callers, even if they were brothers, were forgotten as food was partaken of. Well earned food — for both of us.

My life was changed by an old school mate of my husband's. This fellow breezed into our house one night about 8.30. He breezed out the following morning at about four o'clock. I found his non-stop flow of conversation absolutely fascinating. He was tall, fair with blue eyes, not unlike Peter Gilmore, the film star who played James Onedin in the television serial *The Onedin Line.* I rather fancy Peter so needless to mention his double got my full attention.

Your man was a Times and Motions Expert for factories. He explained how various methods have been tried to get better and faster work out of employees in his factory. He said there are at least ten ways of doing a job. any job — down to tying your laces in your shoes. The jobs in the factory are tried out from all angles and timed to the very last second. The fastest method is then naturally adopted. He had travelled half way round the world visiting different countries to study their working methods.

There is a very close watch kept on employees reaction to colour-schemes, music, non-alcoholic drinks and recreation periods. In one factory, he visited, in Germany, there is a padded floored recreation room for the ladies. They lie full length on this floor for ten minutes mid-morning and mid-afternoon. Another factory has a basketball room for the men's resting time. They have a strenuous game twice daily to loosen up their muscles and their brains.

By four o'clock I was a Time and Motions Expert in the making. A real do-it-yourself effort. I could hardly wait to get up next morning to start timing the jobs. Even down to cleaning out the budgies cage. I was amazed to find it took seven minutes. My electric kettle took four minutes to boil; to really scour the bath, toilet and washbasin in the bathroom, clean the tiles and window, vacuum the carpet and mats, ten minutes; dust the thousand and one books in our front room, shine the furniture and fireplace, vacuum the carpet and throw a few flowers in a vase, fifteen minutes.

With a clean house and a clear conscience I threw myself bodily down on the floor of the living room for a rest! Just like the ones in the factory.

I tore through the bedrooms like a human hurricane. I scrubbed the kitchen to within an inch of its life, I shone the tiles and surrounds. The units came into contact with my cleaning rag — the kettle — the cooker. The budgie was fired in and out of his cage. I scoured it out. Changed the ~aper — cleaned the bars and perches. Swilled the two)ldfish in and out of the washingup bowl — shone their nk. Fed the three livestock. Then I flung myself down on he floor for another rest. The whole place shone.

Each day since that eye opener of timing the jobs I am flying. I do the everyday jobs automatically — cleaning. cooking, washing and sewing. One day a week I do the charring bit — I watch the clock and fly around like a broomless witch. Actually I am more modern in the witch's class — I am armed with a vacuum cleaner, spray on polishes and air freshners. I fling open the windows as each room is done. All smells of stale air, air freshners, polishes, fly killers and (I hope not) — B.O. disappear out to add to the pollution of the air!

The days when I had to unfurl cobwebs is gone. No longer do I feel, in my innermost heart, that my semi — detached resembles the back drop for some of the gruelling scenes of *Wuthering Heights*. Now I am mistress of all I survey. I have conquered the race against dirt and dust. The day, Monday, for the charring I don a clean apron, tie back the bit of hair nicely. My slacks may have seen better days, but they are clean. I dress the part of a self-employed mistress of a well kept home. Tuesday to Sunday I can take it easy and generally arse around my shining home.

I used be jaded — not from the jobs I was doing — but, from the very thought of the jobs I was not doing. Now I practically annoy myself I am so super efficient.

The flinging oneself flat for rests is very beneficial to one's health and well-being. I was at it for ages before my husband caught me in the act so to speak. He took one pennyworth of me stretched full length on the hearth-rug. There lay the love of his life, pale and wan. I am always pale and wan — it is my natural colouring. He tore out the front door, across the road with him. He nearly took a one's door bell out by the roots. She had been a nurse before her marriage. He brought her back with him. They were joined by a few passing neighbours. Just as my rest time was up in they trotted in our front door.

I explained I had been taking a little rest. I was in perfect health and there was no need to ring for an undertaker or anyone else connected with one's last journey. They looked at me and smiled. I know that their brain were registering the fact that, God help us, I really was not all there after all. Was I not proving it time and time again with my rather peculiar, to say the least of them, idiosyncracies.

You can keep your coffee and biscuits. You can keep your eleven o'clock breaks. Just adding to your waistlines you are. Me? I just down tools and lower my bag of bones on the nearest mat.

For fear of anyone getting a fright this past year or two I have thought of a great plan. I have a card. On this card I have written, in nice plain, copperplate writing a very clear message. It reads. 'Your Mother is not Dead but Sleepeth.' I pin this card to my bosom when I now take a rest. No one will take me for a corpse now. When not in use I keep the card in my apron pocket. It is always ready for use. To an outsider this kind of carry on may seem rather odd. My crowd take no heed of me really. They just walk over my prostrated body, if I happen to be in their path. They know, and I know, that 'Mother' shall rise again. No one can really teach you to do housework efficiently. Experience is truely the best teacher. Looking at the curtained windows of houses that I pass it often occurs to me how do the women behind these curtains do their work. Do they love it? Do they hate it? How do they do it? Have they learned knacks, like me, over a period of years? Single people think running a home is a yummy way of passing your middle years, so to speak. My single friends, often ask me what do I do all day. The way they ask gives the implication that I do damn all. I do loads — it may be just that I give the impression of being a lady of leisure. Public Park Gardeners would give you the impression that they are only tipping around the place with a hoe. You do the same in your garden and it is tiring work. I suppose if you do not understand the rudiments of a job you just take it for granted that, if a person is not actually dropping dead, they are just sailing along.

CHAPTER

16

Another myth single girls believe in is that there is only one man in a married woman's life. Believe me there are millions. If I were never to go outside my door there would be still droves of males in my life. I am just talking now about chatting with the opposite sex. I am sure one could have sexual liaisons if one felt in the mood. I never did—no one actually asked me in so many words—you know? Rather a slap to my sex image but they say you cannot win 'em all! One or two advances would not have gone astray?

Across my chaste white path have crossed many many postmen. So what? Well—I am just numberin them among my men. One fellow really intrigued me He used deliver maybe three letters—one at a time on th same day. He would come to the door, put in the letter - the first, then he would trot out to the bike and bring in another, then he would bring in the third. I am always on the look out for letters and usually met him at the door. God, I thought to myself, your man is trying to get off his mark. Into my hand he would put the letters, one at a time. Was it the magic of my touching his hand with mine I wondered? If I did not meet him he would ring the bell. Although we have a normal honest to God letter-box, I began to get afraid of him when he started ringing the bell and giving me letters for some of the neighbours. God help him, I thought to myself, he has it really bad. Not to insult him I used take the letters. When he had cleared out of the estate I would deliver them in to their right owner's letter-boxes.

Then the day came when my bubble of romance broke. One morning I saw the darkly dressed figure coming up the drive. In popped two envelopes in the letter-box. I ran in to the front room and looked out the window. There was my brave lover, as I thought, sorting his letters with great finesse. He looked different. Was he a new fellow? No. He was our man all right but he had a new pair of glasses on him. He had not been sure of the names or addresses because without the glasses he could not see properly. Still it kept me going for weeks.

My milkman is another of my callers, having been running in my kitchen door every Thursday for years for his money. He has filled me in on his life story for years and years (his family have grown up and got married and he is now a grandfather). I always thought he was a great dog man, talking for years about taking 'Fluffy' for a walk after tea. Over the years 'Fluffy' has had little colds and he has been worried. Next call I would get another instalment of the condition of 'Fluffy.' About two years ago I had the misfortune to ask what type of dog 'Fluffy' was. Jesus — 'Fluffy' was my milkman's wife! The mistake was glossed over beautifully by your man but I can still feel the sweat breaking out on me when I think of my fau pas.

A few months ago a lady called to collect some stuff for a Jumble Sale. She is a resident of the road that runs behind our house. She is on this and that committee and one of the female backbones of the town, collecting old clothes for itinerants, toys for children in hospitals and parcels for the poor and aged. Anyway, this day she called I asked her in. We sat in my dining room. The sun shone in on my shining room. Everything was laid out like an altar. A jersey I was in the throas of knitting laid on one of the chairs, in a tidy bundle. A terrific floral arrangement sat on the television. The back garden lay serene outside on its dark brown earth, spring flowers swaying in the gentle breeze. I suggested a cup of tea, it was around eleven and she jumped at the idea. I produced my tray on wheels, my best china, my tea and home-made buns. Delicious little delicacies with coconut and icing — really the works.

I could see your one being more and more impressed by the minute. I naturally — only being human — was thrilled. We chatted about this and that. Then she started praising me on my beautiful home. It is not everyone, she assured me, kept a home on the par of mine. The gardens, exquisite, perfect. I was so smart too. Then she started telling me about certain — what you might call 'scarlet women' of our side of the town. Some of these ones were in school with me. As long as they keep away from my man they can go to bed with the Bishop for all I care. I listened—some was stale news—more of it was fresh. They seemingly sleep around, wife swap, go for mucky week-ends and that kind of thing. All I can say is no better women. I did not say that to her, of course, what a fool I'd be and she thinking I was a model wife and mother. How could anyone, any fully grown mature woman, lead a life like that she asked me? What kind of animals were they? How could they face their husbands? How could they face us — the world? No words could describe such a terrible carry on. She ate her way through the plate of cakes and drank two cups of tea and gave me a lecture on loose living. I was beginning to feel I was not livʼ _ Such fun your ones were supposed to be having.

In the middle of it all my milkman called as usual. She told me in low tones she thought there was a man in the kitchen. She must have heard him cough or something.

I ran out and sure enough there was my milkman. He ran around the kitchen. As usual he ran over to the budgies cage. He has a budgie himself for years and loves them.

'Hello, you beautiful little bird,' he bellowed at my poor old budgie. 'Are you not the sweetest little pudding in the whole world with your lovely little legs. Give Charlie your weekly little kissy. Yum, yum, yum, you little pet. I love to see you every Thursday, don't I, Pet?'

The bird only looked at him in amazement. He always does; cannot get over this monologue every week, so he can't.

I handed him his money and he ran out the hall. 'Cannot wait — this week I can't', he continued on his way out the door, 'Bye —'Bye.'

When I closed the front door on him I nearly tripped over my woman. She was on my heels in the hall. She had my Jumble clutched on her heart and she just looked at me. She had heard every word Charlie had screamed in the kitchen.

100

I know how Caesar looked when he pronounced the immortal,'Et tu Brutus?'

'He was talking to the budgie,' I explained hastily. Even to my ears it sounded like a lie.

Your one continued to stare at me as if I had crawled out from some nearby stone.

'Thank you for the Jumble stuff,' said she all high and mighty. With that she sailed off, full of cakes, tea and yet more gossip. I can still see her in other houses partaking of their hospitality. I suppose she is still regailing people with the story of the milkman and the one in the estate in front of her road.

Oh, Jesus, look how easy it is to loose one's reputation. You were there, Jesus, and You know I am not guilty, My Lord.

Tuesdays and Fridays I am entertained by four gorgeous men. These are my four bin-men. They officially come between 10.30 and 11.30. Sometimes they come earlier and other times they do not arrive until after 3 o' clock. If they are here between their official hour they are relaxed and full of the joys of life. They are all singing together. A chorus of angels with the thump of the bins against the lorry for drums. This sounds marvellous and it is. I would say it would be really something if they were all singing the same song. But they never do. They just do not feel like it I suppose.

One fellow is a great pop fan, he has the very latest songs before you would even hear them on the radio. He does a king of sponsored programme He plugs the various soap powder packets and canned foo s that float out of the bins. He also does requests. He might spot the one from No 1/3 peeping out the window and he will yell, 'For my mother who lives at No 18 (mentioning our estate), I would like you to sing '*My Ding-a-ling.*'

That song is one of his favourites actually. He does a kind of action song and dance act with it. The older ladies of the estate run when they see him. No granny is safe with him around —he thinks nothing of dancing with any old lady he sees. There is one old girl who, I'd swear, waits for him. She often passes a comment to him. You would see him looking at her and then breaking his sides laughing. I would imagine that in her he meets his match. The rest of us dread him.

The second fellow — Paul — he hums. He has real high fallutin' taste. Some days we get Ravels Bolero. He hums that every bit as loud as the other fellow sings. Other days we might get a rendering of *The Nutcracker Suite* complete with the Sugar Plum Fairy doing her dance to the Waltz of the Flowers. His repertoire seems endless, and he does not spare us.

Patrick, he is a real Irishian. He'd have the *Mountains of Mourne sweeping down to the Sea* as regular as clockwork. He waltzes around the road with a dirty bin up to his cheek and gives a rendering of *I'll Take you Home Again, Kathleen*. He has a really pure voice. *Oh, Danny Boy* as he sings it often bring tears to my eyes. I think he knows that too. If I go out for the bin he starts off at the top of his lungs. He will lean romantically on my gate pier and bellow it into my face.

Mr O'Shea drives the truck. He honks the horn which is very rusty and sounds it. Like a chesty old horse, that hooter is. On days it is lashing raining he never fails to greet one and all: 'Grand sunny day, God bless you.' He has only one song and he sings it over and over and over again. It is that lovely old one, *Somewhere the Sun is Shining*. Sometimes he puts in his own words. It is well worth listening to, when you can catch it over the din of the other three artists. They really are a gas crowd and an addition to any women's life.

If they came early, they shout and ring doorbells. If you have the misfortune to appear in a dressing-gown they will all stop singing. The comments are really choice. 'Ha-Ha, caught you out. You ducked back to bed and the poor fool's gone out to work.'
'Are you lonely above there in the bed? Would you like one of us to mind you until the old man comes home?' One of the women across the road was in hospital last year and her mother came to stay to mind the children. The mother appeared in her dressing gown and rollers and no end of a nightdress to the ground. The boys gave her an

awful time altogether. She was in from the country and I would say no one ever shouted at her before. She nearly died with shock. Mr O'Shea carried back her bin personally and rang the bell and asked her to kiss him. The daughter was lucky the old lady did not get a stroke there and then.

After a few turns she got quite used to them and used to give back as good as she got. On the last day of her two month stay, out she came and kissed them all. All us young ones were tut-tutting and shouting at them that they were the permissive society and we would get the Parish Priest to bless the truck! The old lady was thrilled. Signs on she has been back three times since.

God, if they are late though it is terrible. All the dogs of the estate and all the neighbouring estates play havoc with the bins. Our weekly supply of tinned food are rolling around the road, toilet rolls fly under the wheels of speeding cars and potato peelings under the paws of these awful dogs. No end of catches or large stones on the bins save them from being toppled by these animals. It is a great relief to hear our 'Boys' coming down the hill, hearing them honking and hooting and singing well before they are seen.

When we came to the estate first we were damned from commercial door-to-door salesmen. They would try to sell anything from electric floor cleaners to damp carpets. These fellows could get quite narky if you refused their wares. I used to say, in the beginning, 'Sorry, we have too many commitments!' That, at least at that time was the truth. Then I struck on a better plan. I told them, without batting an eyebrow, that I was only staff. They doffed their caps and left. There was no question in their minds that I was fooling. Now I have raised my niche a little higher. I tell them I am only baby-sitting.

One night two Jehovah Witnesses called. I had the children in bed. My husband was gone over for my mother to baby-sit. We were going out to a dinner dance and I was done up to the knockers. Eye shadow, pencilled in lower lashed and an Elizabeth Taylor beauty spot. I use my face as a canvas and paint in youth, vivacity and sex appeal. I might never make it as an artist, but if you saw me an hour before going out and an hour after I am out, you would not believe it was the same person. Of course, it takes loads of practice, but I am years at it. Anyway, as I was saying, I opened the door to the two buckos. I told them I was not interested in changing my religion actually. Then when they asked to step inside, I told them I was only the baby-sitter. One fellow asked what time would the owners of the house be back and I said about midnight. Would I be going home then, he asked me. Yes, I told him.

When we arrived home from the dinner dance wasn't your man sitting on the wall waiting. I had to smuggle myself in and my mother out behind his back. While my husband was driving her home my heart was in my mouth for fear your man would trail in and knife me or something. He went off eventually. The moral to that story I suppose is that one should be made up fully at all times. If one wishes to upset men's equilibrium one must be ready to face the onslought of their emotions. All these men callers might not add up to the height of glamour and tempt my single friends to change their single state. Yes, I suppose life can be a bit dull behind the lace curtains. With a little imagination one can make it very exciting though. Remember the postman?

Outside the house, men can play a big part in one's life too — as a married woman, I mean. There is a lot of truth in the saying: 'Have a goose you will get a goose'. Once you are safely married the men feel quite safe. They find it great fun to flirt away to their heart's content. They know in their hearts and souls you will not take them seriously. They will not have to take you home afterwards and they go off feeling they are real Don Juans. If men tell me I am lovely I am delighted. I take it as a real compliment to me and my Maker. Especially me. If you had to go to the trouble I have to go to make myself lovely, you would appreciate it too.

I always seem to get tied up with some man no matter where we go. Glory be to God, I do not know what kind of face I have, but it draws men like honey to bees. Are these hunks of manhood whispering sweet nothings to me?

They are in their hats. Honest to God, I know more about male hernias than any qualified doctor. The youngest of them are the worst. They will fill me in, without sparing me, on how they pulled such a muscle. Their hands fly about in the air, their breath gets fast as they demonstrate how they were attacked, how they fell and how they suffered. They even give copies of their moans and groans. More of these guys giving demonstrations and people will think they are working out under my massive sexual charms! The old daddy fellows are even more entertaining — they would produce their hernias and show them to you at the drop of a hat. Needless to mention I do not encourage them. They also have slipped discs or 'chests'. Bad chests, you know. Anyway, I listen to every word they utter and enjoy them all. The funny thing about it, these same fellows will eventually make it back to talk to my husband and tell him that I am the most intelligent woman they have ever talked to. To them it is immaterial that I smell nice, I look nice, I am nice. The mere fact that I am listening to them is enough. Because I do not shut them up or laugh at them, they think I am the most gorgeous woman in the room. I love to hear the drone of a man's voice. I may not at all times follow what he is saying. Politics, world affairs, etc., these are above my head. Most times I can follow the stream of conversation though. An odd word, here and there, and you have a happy man.

Women — well — I have been one too long to enjoy listening to them. Most times, they are like myself, they are only talking off the tops of their heads. They boast like nobody's business. Their husbands are the best in the world. Their children are the lovliest. Their homes are second to none. They give me their medical histories, in full detail. Confinements — God, stitch by stitch. They insist on telling me their innermost secrets. I get full vent of their feelings of frustration, anger and loneliness. Do I think their children are bright enough? After they telling me in the same breath they were the brightest in the world. Would I consider their husbands to be inclined to stray from the straight and narrow? Six breaths before hand I had to listen to a list of their husbands good points, faithfullness being number one on the list. How could they improve their looks? How could they improve their homes? How could they improve their marriages? At times I feel like a walking agony column. I can be of no use to these ones. For God's sake aren't I up to my neck myself with all my own questions. Who can I ask? Who will answer my questions? How do I straighten myself out? The men are too bloody busy telling me about their physical disorders and the women are too busy telling me about their mental ones. God knows, no wonder I have written this bloody book, imagine trying to tell people my memoirs? Holy Mother, they would switch me off mentally in two minutes flat! Do you ever get really entangled in a terrific story. I often have. I have some misfortune button-holed. I go on and on about some incident in my faraway childhood. Maybe it is something out of my far away youth. It does not matter—to me it is either excruciatingly funny or heartbreakingly sad. I nearly work out in a fit so that they will not miss one moment of the drama of my story. Then I take a second off from my acting and look at my listener. They have a glazed look over their eyes. Their faces have a secret closed look. They are not listening. There is nothing worse than the sensation of knowing you are switched off. I try never to do it myself. Although sometimes I am in a semi-coma from boredom or tiredness. I used to talk a lot in company, now I do not though. I have become a listener instead. Someone in my family said to me one day: 'You make me vomit going on, on and on about our Grandmother and the lot of them.'

I suppose I used to bore people. I thought I was entertaining them. You know when gaps come in conversations. Especially if there are visitors and you are raking your brains for something to say. No one seems to have anything of interest. The guests are too polite to stand up and go home. Then I come out with an anecdote. This gets their attention and I think up another one. I suppose it is a case of molaigh on oige—praise the young kind of thing. I forget myself and branch off on a monologue and afterwards then . . . well, I get eaten for boring the pants off everyone. That shuts me up for ages then I am as bad as ever again in no time. Not being sorry for myself or anything – it is not worth shutting me up now really! Pardon me for not sparing you the drama of my numbered days.

CHAPTER

17

They say you should never try to turn the clock back and that you should never, never return to the scene of a crime.

Well, a few weeks ago I did something like that. I returned to my Alma Mater. I do not know why and I could honestly have said that if I lived to be a hundred I could never say why I did it. I returned for the annual reunion.

I saw the usual advertisement in the paper about it. This appears annually and each year I ignore it. I usually turn the page and mutter, 'The old whores — what a hope!' and immediately I feel happy.

It was to be on a Sunday on which I knew my husband was going to a match with his brother. I dropped the children over to my mother and set off walking to the school. As I went along the road I thought of all the days, year in year out, I made the same journey. A shiver came over me as I thought of the terror which used fill me on my journeys to that school. With each step memories of those terrible days came back one after the other. Mother Brenda battering my right hand and my left one. I saw a mental picture of her throwing my bunch of flowers in the bin, flowers that were jewel fresh. I thought her action was a downright sin. It was the last time I brought flowers to her for the May Altar. Her pets were allowed arrange their flowers in vases on the altar, but not me. I was in a fierce temper that day but the tears that scalded my eyes were of pure bewilderment. Why did she dislike me so? How often had I asked myself that question.

As I approached the huge grey gates my heart started to race. The gates were wide open but like in a nightmare my feet felt leaden. My back was hurting me, should I turn back I wondered.

The warm spring sunshine comforted me. I began to feel quite chirpy again as I marched along. I could feel nuns peeping out of various shining windows. I was reminded of that poem we once learned. The one about the eyes out of the mud cabins. What harm, I suppose there was not a nun at any of the windows at all. When we used to be going in along that drive on the way to school, they used be on the look-out all right. If you kicked the pebbles you would hear hammering at one of the windows and you would know you had been spotted.

As I went along I spotted two figures under one of the conker trees. One was a nun and the other was a man. As I got on a level with them I could see them properly. She was a lovely little thing, a cross between Audrey Hepburn and St Theresa, and he was the living, spitting image of Richard Burton.

I studied them as I came along. The little nun threw back her head and went into screams of laughter. The two of them were the picture of youth and health.

As I nearly came on a level with them they stopped their conversation and watched me advancing towards them. I felt like shouting, 'Things is looking up around here,' like the fellow shouted in my last office job when he saw me appearing.

They smiled at me and I said, 'Where is Harry?' 'Harry?' they answered together and looked from one to the other questioningly. They both shook their heads. 'Harry,' I explained. 'He was the gardener here when I was coming to school here'.

They both looked at me blank. I felt I was not alone Rip Van Winkle but his bloody greatgrandmother!

'It doesn't matter,' I said and I continued on my way. I left the two of them deep in conversation in the shade of the old conker tree. I rounded the front of the Convent. The wide expanse of hockey fields and hard courts spread out in front of me.

I stood and surveyed the grounds for a few minutes. I walked and ran around these grounds so many years ago. I was so full of life then. I was so full of dreams. Now I felt the weight of years and pain on top of me. The pain in my back squeezed me in its grip like an unrelenting vice. How would I put up with it? Why did I have to bear it? The sunshine mocked me. I felt like the Old Pensioner to whom W B Yeats gave the lines

> I spit into the face of Time
> That has transfigured me.

I walked towards the front door. My reflection looked back at me. I stood staring at myself: well turned out, well groomed, model of a young matron. I put my finger on the bell. I remembered just in time not to tear it out by the guts as I am inclined to ring our own.

A minute later a lay sister let me in and escorted me down a shiny parquet hall. When the main parlour door was opened, a loud chattering, giggling noise hit me. The smell of perfume was only gorgeous. I focused my never-wear-my-glasses eyes on the throng en masse. Then I edged my way in among the bodies. I saw an empty window sill and sat down. I surveyed the gang at a much better advantage.

They all looked well. Some looked very opulent in fact. There was one slim figure in a scarlet maxi and a real dishy hat perched on the side of her head. Why it was Maggie — Maggie — oh, the second name was gone. Maggie — God, she was the fattest, clumsiest girl I had ever sat beside, all those years ago. A glistening wedding, engagement and eternity ring shone on her perfectly groomed hand.

She used have those nails down to the very quick as she struggled with Euclid. I could still hear her biting and chewing them.

A familiar tinkling laugh drew my eyes off her. I followed the laugh to the other side of the room. A real vivacious blonde threw her arms up in the air and shouted, 'Of course I am the mother of six.' She proceeded to produce a photograph to prove it. I saw it over the shoulders of the one in front of me. The six children smiled out of the photograph and their father was about twelve stone of all right! My God — Anna — Anna — oh, what matter. She was Anna all right. But what a change. She had been the tiniest, mousiest little thing you could ever imagine. You would never hear her voices above a mere whisper but she had a very musical laugh you could not fail to hear. But, I just could not get over the change in her — it was fantastic.

I sat flabbergasted as I named them all in my mind. They had all changed — for the better — and it was unbelievable.

There were a few strange nuns floating around. They were handing out cups of tea and savouries. Someone put theirs on the sill beside me as they examined someone elses photographs. I ate them with great relish and drank the tea for good measure. Then a nun brought out our class photograph and there were squeals of laughter as each one recognised herself.

I slipped out and made a lone pilgrimage to my old class room. I stood in the corridor. Many is the time I had stood there in the past. I had been flung out of the class for dreaming on countless occasions. I searched the doorpost and at long last found what I was looking for. My name - ELLEN. It stood out through all the coats of paint and varnish. I had scratched it on one day with a hair clip. It had been my one and only act of defiance.

I went into the beautiful chapel. I knelt in my old favourite corner and for the first time, since I entered the front gates, I relaxed.

Tulips and irises were on the altar. They are among the flowers we have set in our gardens. They are the flowers the house was filled with when I came home with my two children. It seemed just right that they should be on the altar on this day of my return. The altar cloth was the same one — or it had the same message as it always had long ago: Wilth Thou Not Watch One Hour With Me. 'Jesus,' I whispered 'I haven't time to stop one hour here; where is Harry?' Naturally He did not reply. I stayed a few more minutes and reluctantly left the peacefullness of the tiny chapel.

I made my way back to the girls, my old pals, my contemporaries. Girls how are you?

When I re-entered the parlour I noticed the little nun who had been under the conker tree. She was wheeling a nun in a wheel-chair among the girls. The girls were taking no notice of the old nun. I took a seat again on the window sill and studied her. She was old and very wrinkled. She had obviously had a very severe stroke. Her right arm was badly twisted so was her face. She looked around from one to another of the milling crowd of women.

Something about her struck me as being familiar. I had seen people with strokes before but she was the worst I had ever seen. As my eye caught hers, I recognised her. I left my seat and went over to her. I stood in front of her and looked at her. She stared back at me with the helpless look of a trapped animal. I knelt beside her twisted body and took her hand in mine. It was lifeless.

'Mother Brenda,' I said to her, 'how are you?'

She only looked at me and her mouth moved soundlessly. She mouthed my name but no sound came out.

'Mother Brenda has lost her speech,' the little nun explained in a whisper, 'She is not so well. I must take her to her bedroom now.'

Mother Brenda looked at me without wavering her glance. The look in her eyes looked familiar. It is the look I can see in the mirror. She was not staring at me — she was staring at Death.

As the nun wheeled her away a weight lifted from my heart. My years of hating her were over; all I could feel was a deep compassion. She was just a mass of twisted humanity. Anything she did, she did because she thought she was doing right.

I realised then that I owe her quite a lot. All the things I tackled during my life and mastered, I owe to her. She was always the one to tell me in school I would fail. To prove her wrong I used to succeed. I kept at everything until I got it right. I had got into the habit from dealing with her. All my life I have done my best just not to give her the satisfaction of crowing over me in my failure.

My grandmother always knew when a person was going to die soon – she explained that she could smell the earth off them. I have that gift too and am rarely wrong. Mother Brenda was definitely going to die soon. One could not feel sorry for her because she would at last be free from the broken cage of her twisted body. I am always afraid that other people have the gift of smelling the earth off people. Signs on, I drown myself in perfume for fear they would learn my secret. Talcum powder is dashed on with wild abandon and perfume is swilled down the neck of my dress. I am like a walking chemists shop — well, the cosmetic counter anyway.

The girlfriends of my long lost youth were still ooohing and aahing over the class photograph. I could see it being passed around. The difference the years made in all these ones was remarkable. Were these fine figures of women really the little ones who stared out of the photograph? It was very hard to believe. I looked at myself in the reflection of a bookcase. The face was kind of blurred but it was all right. The smart spring coat covered my slim body. My legs looked all right and the blue shoes were modern. I was just as nice as the best of them really.

What had I done with myself since I was in their company? I had held down a few jobs. I had acquired a husband and two children. I was capable of running a home — I was quite a good bargain really, I supposed. Well, I did not make a fierce hash out of my life, I had done my best and enjoyed it. Maybe some people got annoyed with me over the years. God wasn't I annoyed to death practically, at times, by people, too. I am not a paragon of virtue I told myself. If put on a pedastal I would topple off in five minutes flat. Still, I was as good as the next. I too had improved with age, like these contemporaries of mine. Even wine improves with age!

Someone placed the class photograph in my hand. I stood staring at it. There I sat, in black and white, in the second row. A delicate looking young one with two enormous scared eyes. A very plain, very skinny, very non-descript twelve year old. I felt sorry for this child that I was. Did the world really seem that bad? Was I that scared? It did. I was. I knew because I was there. It still scares me, and I knew as I stared into my own childlike face, I shall always feel lost.

As I savoured these anything but cheerful thoughts, the picture was nearly swept out of my hand. This one as big as a horse was taking off a blue maxi coat and nearly knocking about three of us down in the process.

'Sorry honey,' she said to me with a slight American

accent.

I looked at her closely. Under the layers of make-up and good feeding I recognised her.

'Betty,' I said to her as I caught her sleeve, 'Betty, you remember me?'

She had been my best friend for years. She had left after Intermediate, too. She had met a real Sugar Daddy of a fellow. He had fallen madly in love with her and she with him. They got married — about a million guests, about fifty miles of red carpet. — and went off to New York. They lived happily ever after and reared a family of three.

She turned and looked at me. False eye-lashes flapped in my face as she peered at me from underneath them. Then she left out a real maniacal laugh. She threw her arms around me in a big bloody bear hug. She had not changed much from the times we were in school. She used be always jumping and shouting then, too, like a big friendly dog.

'Jasus,' she roared into my face, 'Jasus, if it isn't Ellen. Jasus you haven't changed a bit.'

'Ellen,' she added for good measure, 'you are the same as the day we left school. With that she tore the photograph out of my hand and ran across the parlour with it to another of our pals.

I looked at her as she pointed at all the ones in the picture and pointed at them now as full grown women. She pointed over at me and waved. For the first time in my life I felt lonely in a crowd. I did not envy them all their affluence. I have plenty of money. I envied them their future, no matter what they held for them. I whipped a savoury off a plate as I passed. I chewed it thoughfully as I went out into the sunshine.

Was I going to get real morose, I asked myself. The answer was yes. Was I going to be a right idiot and depress everyone with my thoughts? The answer was no. Scared and frightened as I was of the world, I was the life and soul of the classes I was in. I was up to every mischief under the sun during those school-days of mine. Remember the fellows who used be lined up outside the gates after school? I had my fair share of them as escorts home. I rarely had to carry my own books. I always got home on the bar of some bike. Maybe I was not extraordinary at the book learning, but the fellows? Yes, they appreciated my brains — or something anyway. At once I cheered up.

I went down past the hockey fields, past the hard courts, and past the grotto. I went into the grotto to have a look at St. Bernadette. There was still a chip off her nose. I had pegged a stone at her one day. Luckily I was not caught. Just the devil got into me and I watched with horror as the stone hit her. The chip came off like a slice of butter. There was never a mention of it by the nuns — they probably thought some bird pecked it off.

I entered the nuns' cemetary. The graves lay in the spring sunshine. Crocus and wild primroses bloomed. Daffodils stood proudly at regular intervals. It was tidy and clean and peaceful. I read all the tombstones. God, our old Reverend Mother was laid to rest — bitch. Mother Mary the singing nun; she would be handy for a few choruses in heaven, if she ever got there, I thought. Mother Angelo, the cookery nun maybe she poisoned herself. She had not a clue about cookery, God help her, nearly poisoned the boarders with the meals she prepared. She was a nice nun. Mother Cecelia the elecution nun, Jesus, I said to myself, they are all dead — the whole bloody lot of them.

Mother Cecelia was as mad as a hatter. She had a name or all the conker trees and used to talk to them. In beautiful modulated tones, naturally! She used to talk to the flowers and the old ass adored her. She used to have an odd chat with me, too. She often told me I would go far as I had imagination — one would be better to have smothered in one's mothers womb as not to have imagination. At the time I did not know what a womb was but I reckoned I had something anyway. Mother Bernadette — the knickers nun as she was called. Poor old Mother B, she was the sewing nun. We used to have to sew a garment every year. Every class, every year, she would have us sewing the same type of garment: a different one each year of course, each trip the same garment, a knickers — and as fine pair if ever you wanted to fit yourself, your parents and grandparents into it at the same time. For a two legged elephant they would be beautiful. For us, the FEMMES FATALES of the future, they were dynamic. One year, Mother B as we called her, suffered her first nervous breakdown. She had about six during my school career and they were the highlights of my schooldays, God forgive me.

We all trooped in as usual with our sewing bags under our arms, yards of material for the garments, miles of thread and needles.

Mother B sat at the top of the class as usual, a bit red in the face but the same mad look about her: 'Get out your garments girls', said she.

A few of us did, some of the bold ones kept on whispering.

'Get out the garments', she tried again.

Very few moved. She caught up a huge tailors scissors and made a run at us.

'Get out your bloody knickers or I will kill the lot of ye,' she roared,

We scattered; me and three others jumped out the nearest window. Lucky for us we were on the ground floor. Harry ran in and help was got. Mother B was missing for a good while.

She came back tranquil and happy, still a bit mad looking. On we went with our elephants under-pinnings.

For another breakdown Mother B thought she was a cat and she climbed up a tree and sat meowing down at us. Just thinking of her as I looked at her tombstone I got a fit of laughing. I looked around to see that no one was looking. I was alone. A bird whistled over in the corner, A greenish tombstone caught my attention. A grave, rather neglected, too, fronted the tombstone. I walked over still chuckling as I remembered Mother B's adventures. The writing on the tombstone was very scarce, just one word: 'HARRY' – no date, no nothing.

I stood and stared at it. The sunshine dimmed and the laughter died on my lips. This old green tombstone and neglected patch was all that remained of my best friend of my school-days. Tears started to drop out of my eyes. I do not cry out aloud any more. I can watch

116

television with the family or go to the pictures with my husband and cry my heart out. Behind a held-up newspaper, tears can flow unheeded. Time is running out for me you see and I get lonesome.

Harry of the crinkly smile. Harry of the big red stolen apples. Harry, I got out a packet of paper tissues and with spits and tears I cleaned up the tombstone as best I could. I scraped moss off it with a little sharp stone. It was not too bad after all. It was coming clean. I scrubbed at it in my sadness and felt I was channelling my sorrow into a good job. I then got a pointy stick and loosened the earth over the grave. I edged it with a broken rock and got pebbles and marked it out in a rough 6' x 4' as was his rightful portion of ground.

I sat back on my heels and surveyed my work. His grave looked very neat and very bare. I looked at the nuns' graves and they bursting with spring flowers. Up I got and searched for a shovel shaped stick. An odd crocus here and an odd daffodil there would not be missed. I went about and dug up a flower off each one nearly. Well, the ones with the most anyway. I set to and planted Harry's grave with my spoils. I dug up wild primroses out of the hedging and edged his grave with them. These flowers would come up every spring and multiply. The nuns' graves would be abundant with flowers too. 'Poor old devils, may they rest in peace', I prayed as I robbed their flowers. One mangey flower off each old girl would not be missed.

At last my job was done. I stood up and surveyed my work once more. Harry's grave was the nicest in the place. A bird whistled in the nearby bushes. He could not wait for me to leave to see if I had dug up any worms for his tea. Harry would not be lonely with all the little birds in the bushes — he always used draw my attention to their different warblings. He knew each type of bird by sight. Poor old Harry. I gave one last look around and went out the gate shutting it carefully behind me. 'God be good to Harry' I prayed to myself, 'and the nuns — well, I leave them to Your Good Self.' After all He made them and let Him be responsible for them, I mused.

I walked back up the path I had gone down. I was feeling very tired from my emotions and my labours. The sun was still shining. After an emotional upset, it never fails to surprise me that the sun is still shining and the world is still the same. I could be torn apart inside and all is the same in the outside world. With the mental battles that I draw on myself at times I am just as well pleased there is no outward show of them. The bloody place would be like as if a bomb hit it if the outside world was to match my inner feelings at times!

I walked past St Bernadette with the chipped nose. Past the hard courts and the hockey fields. Before I got into the school gardens I took a little rest on a bit of grass. I just slumped real unladylike onto the grass and put my back up against a tree stump.

'Oh, Jesus,' I commented, 'I am terribly tired; I feel like as if I am going to die here and now from pure exhaustion.' That comment did the trick. The very thought of dying in the school nearly finished me. Up I got and on I went. Out past the buildings and on under the conker trees. There was no sign of my friends — they were all gone home probably hours. It was very nearly six o'clock by the the sound the angelus bells of the nearby church was making. I got to the school gate and the Richard Burtony gardener was leaning against them.

As I approached he smiled at me 'Lose yourself Miss?' he asked.

'No,' I smiled into his handsome face,' I think I found myself.'

CHAPTER

18

One of the greatest bogeys, I think, in a young housewife's life is shopping for the family meals. For the ordinary run of us, budgeting has to be strictly adhered to. With all the problems of your married state, you have to make ends meet. Some are better than others at it. I was never too bright at figures, but after my vast experience at cooking my accounts, I could now give lessons in bookkeeping. In the beginning I found it a fierce strain.

From the very start, I insisted on a regular wage each week. This was strictly for food. A small personal allowance was added which I spent on presents, clothes and anything personal. Both of these allowances have grown over the years. My husband and I have discussed our finances openly. If I felt a rise was necessary, I would apply to him for one. If he got a rise in his job, I would put in for my percentage of it. This sounds all very hard-boiled egg type of transactioning, but it has been done in the very nicest way. I usually discuss finances when I am dressed for the part. A frilly nightdress will get better results than browbeating the poor misfortunate and I dressed for a Mother's Meeting. Covered from neck to knee will get you nowhere — even at a Mother's meeting! It pays, I feel, in all aspects of dealings with men to pander to their weaknesses. Show me a man who will refuse anything when approached in the right manner by a one lightly perfumed and lightly clad. Where on earth is there a man who cannot resist a bit of temptation on the side? He will part with the money eventually, you might as well let him enjoy it. If you know of a man who refuses to be led astray by frills and the like — you are married to him maybe? — God, keep him. I, personally, would not know what to do with him. How you would get a pound a week extra out of him would be a mystery to me.

In the beginning of each marriage money is mostly on the tight side. When the rosy spectacles of love have faded a little, things could get bad. For the start you could produce any kind of a meal really. Your man would be so taken up with the thoughts of being so lucky to get you he would not notice what he is eating. You flitting about in his kitchen is sufficient to fill him up emotionally. He cannot wait to take you in his arms. Could he lure you back to bed he wonders. Would you think he is some awful kind of beast? Go back into his arms, into his bed, if you are asked. Relax — enjoy yourself, duckey. Some fine day this wonderful man of yours will give a roar of a bull out of him because you again produce sausages and mash. Prices will soar. You will splurge on wine for Sunday or do something with the housekeeping money. You will be rightly up it, so to speak. In between rises, things can get tight — what the hell can you do? Well you might ask. We have all been in the same boat. I remember one day I put a red rose in a vase on the table for the dinner. Knives and forks sparkled, the floor was washed the kitchen shone. We sat down to partake of our meal. The red rose caught my man's eye. Was I getting romantic, artistic or just arty in my old age? He looked at it again as I hoped he might. He ate his dinner silently as the rose fascinated him. So well it might; that is why I put it there. He was so taken up watching that the greenfly did not fall into his glass of milk he did not notice the cold meat with the potatoes and veg. His 'afters' were eaten as he concentrated on the suicidal little insect. If you want to take eyes off the plate, produce a greenfly-infested floral arrangement. One greenfly more or less in the meal will only add protein. The main thing with the economical meals is presentation. Cook the arse off cheap cuts of meat and serve with curry sauce or something. Present the stuff nicely and daintily on the plates. Your man will think you are a reincarnated Mrs Beaton. Get a few professional cookery classes or get a good cookery book. After a few years the lean times will have passed and you will be away at a hack. Grow your own vegetables and herbs, you will have double satisfaction then. Lean times can be got over with a little imagination.

Shops are no help to housewifes either. They seem to vie with each other to be dearer than dear. I usually

leaning on the counter, staring into space. He was tall, greying at the temples and had dark blue eyes. I somehow got the impression I had seen him somewhere before. I could not place him for the life of me. Then I had another look at the packets of liver. But his face rang a bell somewhere in my mind. I had another look at him. He was the image of a man who used to live near us long ago in my youth. Mr McNamara was his name.

'Sure he died ten years before my Dad,' I told myself. Then the penny dropped. Your man, the butcher was 'Macca' - how would I forget him. He was the heart-trob of all my girlfriends.

'God, where did the years go?' I asked myself. Here he was a now greying God, this boy who used to play with us up and down my mother's road. I picked up two packets of liver and handed them to him with a pound note. He never lost his faraway look but at least he took them from me. He did not look at me at all.

'How is the sex life going?' I asked. 'How are the girls, Macca?'

With a very shocked expression, I got Macca's full attention. His dark blue eyes looked straight into mine and his mouth opened but no sound came. He looked searchingly into my face and I just stood and looked back at him.

Then he gave a shout and ran down the length of the cou... he vaulted over the counter (the narrow end) and ran towards me.

'Ellen,' he shouted, 'its you, Ellen — oh, Ellen.'

With that I was enveloped in his arms and his mouth came down on mine in a most ardent kiss. I closed my eyes — I would be a hypocrite to say I did not enjoy it — even early on a Monday morning.

A strangled gasp sounded behind us. I opened my eyes and came out of my erotic dream. The one who had escorted me into the shop was on our heels. She was taking one pennyworth of our compromising position and was getting blue around the mouth from a threatened heart attack. She just continued to gasp — was she not the one who had told me get friendly with the butcher?

Did she consider I was being too serious in my advances? I do not know what she thought but she got a terrible fright seeing us wrapped in each others arms anyway. I could not care less. Me and Macca had met up again after years and years and years. I am sure some of the customers thought us quite mad — him hopping around and shouting how glad he was to see me and what have you.

'Remember the old days,' he was shouting at me. 'Remember my pelvis?'

'Jesus,' I whispered, 'where is your one now?' as I silently prayed she was out of earshot!

'Remember the introductions? Remember the bike in the river? Remember? Remember? Remember?'

We swopped stories of our days long ago and brought each other up to date in less than half an hour.

As I walked home alone — your one, I fear, will never talk to me again — a woman of ill repute I am sure she thinks I am. Kissing a butcher? What next? I remembered the old days and I remembered Macca. I will always remember Macca.

Macca was the only child of an elderly couple. The father died when Macca was about five. His mother went out to work. She worked in an office, she told all the neighbours. She was a cleaning lady but they all let on she was a secretary. Macca was minded by the neighbours during his early years. He spent quite a while at our house while his Mum earned their keep. Sundays he would be the shiniest boy on the road. Daily he was dressed immaculately for school. All our Dads kicked football with him. Anyone going to the circus or the pictures, Macca went too. I remember being about ten years of age and my Dad taking me and Macca to Duffy's Circus. 'God,' Macca gasped during the flying trapeze act, 'isn't she beautiful?'

The star of the show was a one all dressed in spangles with a bun of black hair on top of her head.

'She is old enough to be your mother,' I told him and I suffering from my first pangs of jealously.

Macca just looked at me. From his lordly age of fourteen he probably knew I hated every fibre of her agile body.

What added insult to injury was the fact that my Dad told us she was world famous and had been in the circus since she was two years old. According to the programme he pointed out, she was now twelve.

She moved among the audience later selling tickets for a raffle. I prayed she would get a cold from wearing no coat. Macca followed her every move and I was fit to spit with temper. When we went into the Zoo bit of the circus later I was shaking with temper. Macca put a brotherly arm around me thinking I was afraid of a tiger. I shook him off impatiently —fitter if the tiger ate the one in the spangles, I thought. At that early age I learned that one disadvantage of being a woman is that one is inclined to want to be the cock of the walk, so to speak, all the time. Another female on the scene and one is inclined to count one's curses rather than one's blessings.

I indeed remember Macca. He was tall, thin and fierce athletic. He was a fierce man with the women, even from a very early age. The ones around our place used go mad after him. He was very choosy and the more they chased him the less they saw of him. During the years that I was looking out for my husband — my mental chastity belt days — Macca and I were great buddies. In between romances he would tell me all his troubles. He would walk out from town with me rolling his bicycle with one hand. The other hand would be on my shoulder. It was not romantic tit-bits he was whispering into my shell-like ear. He would be asking me who was such a one. Could I maybe introduce him to the fantastic blonde moved in three doors up? Could I introduce him to the redhead I had been talking to the previous week. I could have his bike for a loan. He would mend mine. He would cut my mothers lawns. He would take me to the pictures - he would take the moon down out of the sky— wipe it on his sleeve and give it to me, if . . . I would tell him the name of such a one. God — I was like a human little black book for that Macca. Not that I didn't get well paid. Wasn't I the envy of the road? Did he not walk me home each day? Was he not a slave to my every nod. He certainly took the bare look off me for years. Most of the neighbours thought it was an oversized attack of puppy-love he had. He had, but not for me.

When he was reaching maturity, at long last, he had some kind of an accident on the bike. Ran into a pole, probably looking after someone (I wouldn't put it past him). Anyway he did a few weeks in hospital. Ones went up to visit him — hundreds of ones. My mother sent me up hot foot with her — or his — favourite biscuits. I sat for hours and listened to his woes. The nurses were all too old. The visiting Moths as he called them were fed up of him. He was not in a position to take them anywhere. I was left as his sole female visitor after the first ten days.

I diligently went in daily. I even pinched flowers from neighbours' gardens to try and cheer him up. Then at long last he came home. I visited him at home. He couldn't walk properly so he refused to come out. None of the girls called — they were gone off with other fellows. His mother was worried — my mother was worried — the whole road of mothers were worried. His sole female admirers were now all the mothers. He would not come outside the door. Ones would laugh at him. Fellows would laugh at him. He was going to stay in to rot.

I tried to get him out: I pleaded, coaxed and bullied him. All to no avail. He was staying put.

One day, on my way to visit him, I met one of the neighbours. She was a real little lady. A Protestant lady who was never without her little white fluffy poodle on a lead. This day she was on her own. I asked her where Madame was and she told me tearfully that 'Madame' could not come out. No more walks for 'Madame' the little old lady practically sobbed.

'Why not,' I asked her.

The subject was seemingly too delicate to discuss. If 'Madame' were to meet other dogs it would be a fate worse than death for her. Also seemingly for her mistress. I asked her why she did not take her out after dark when no other dogs were around and she told me she was afraid of the dark. 'Madame' loved nocturnal strolls, but since 'Madame's' master passed on she had to stay in after dark with her nervous mistress.

As I made my way on to Maccas house I racked my brain for a solution to her problem. I got it – I got a fantastic idea. I raced home and discussed it with my mother. I would take 'Madame' out for walks after dark. I would also get around Macca to accompany me to protect me. After all 'Madame' and I were two very presentable. females. I asked the old lady and she was delighted. Then I faced Macca.

The acting I did that evening you never saw the like of. The Abbey Theatre have lost a great artist in me. With two innocent eyes I put my proposition to Macca and he fell for it—hook, line and sinker.

That night at around ten o'clock I called for Macca. Out he came with two crutches. Then I called for 'Madame' she was all dolled up. Red bow in her fringe and her yellow collar and lead. I set off with the two of them. I was armed with a huge blackthorn stick to protect 'Madame's' virginity and my own (if necessary). There was no fear of me with Macca but no knowing who we might meet on our way. Or so the Protestant lady said, not in so many words, of course.

We set off in great form: me, the poodle and Macca and the crutches. We did fine for half ways around the block and 'Madame' got sleepy. It was way past her bedtime. I carried her in my arms. Another few hundred yards and my other patient conked out. He was not used to fresh air and exercise. He felt groggy. He was tired. He got cross. I dragged him out and he a cripple. The two of us started a row in the middle of the path. We had to go about sixteen rows of houses and turn into our road and go way up to the top to deliver 'Madame' and down half way to deliver me and your man go on a few houses and deliver himself. He sat down on the pavement—folded the crutches up against the wall and refused to budge.

'Get up,' I begged him, 'please get up.'

All he said was, 'no' he was staying there, forever if necessary.

Eventually I got him up; it took nearly an hour. I carried the blackthorn stick and the crutches. I also carried 'Madame' in my arms. I had Macca leaning on my back and shoulders as we crawled home. Christ carrying his Cross must have felt exactly like me. I even told Macca this—might as well be idle, of course. He just crept along at a snail's pace. God was I glad to see the end of him that night.

Next day I met Macca's mother. 'Will ye be off tonight for the little walk again?' she asked hopefully. Along came 'Madame's' mistress and asked me the same question with the same hope in her voice. Way up to visit me brave bucko with the crutches.

'Ellen,' says he 'I'll be ready at 10 sharp tonight for our little walk.'

What could I do with such a crowd?

That night we set off again. 'Madame' lasted a little longer but your man conked out again.

'I will never walk again,' Macca shouted dramatically. 'Blast you—you'll have to,' I shouted back.

'I am going to sit down,' says he. Down he sat. I sat beside him and 'Madame' took the opportunity to roll up in a ball and fall asleep. I could have knocked on any door and got help but I knew Macca would never forgive me. I was not going to be licked. He was told he could walk.

'Get up,' I shouted. He, of course, refused.

'I will kick you,' I said aiming at his pelvic region - I wouldn't have, naturally.

He got up. We set off again. He was very unsteady but he was trying. I had the misfortune to praise his progress and he sat down again.

'Macca . . . ' I warned him lifting my foot off the ground to aim a kick—Up he got.

'Do you know,' he told me quite seriously, 'Florence Nightingale would turn in her grave if she got wind of your treatment to me!'

I ended up with him on my back as we snail-paced home again with our slumbering virgin of a dog.

Night after night the three of us set off. As time wore on Macca's gait improved. He was on one crutch. Then a walking stick. I dispensed with the blackthorn as he could use his on any dog that come our way. We finished up walking together with no stick at all.

'Madame' always came with us and eventually she stayed awake for the full journey. Out of pure habit, one of us would lift her up and carry her and she would snuggle down in our arms as happy as a little sandboy. Those walks were really wonderful. Macca told me all his hopes for the future. We swopped stories about our relations. What we hoped to be when we were adults. What we expected out of us. There was no romance, no strings attached, no nothing. We were just two young people of different sexes and we enjoyed each other's company.

When I look around me these days and see the equivilant of the youngsters today. They are wrapped in each others arms. They are pulling and dragging. Using obscene language. Their speech and their dress is dirty. I ask myself what is becoming to this world of ours. I worry about the children we have brought into the world. Will they lose out on this odd attitude to life the young of today have? We were so much luckier. We had no money – we somehow did not need it. We knew what the word 'friend' meant. We were forming our characters to meet the world in the future. The world was fresh, clean and seemed to be full o fun – in those days.

CHAPTER
19

My grandmother maintained that our Guardian Angels each had a book. In these books they enter our good deeds on one page and our bad deeds on the other. Like the debits and credits in bookkeeping. I would imagine if this story is true that my particular Angel was quite busy during my lifetime. I could just imagine him scratching away with a feather out of his wing, or something like it, for a biro.

When I die I hope to bring a copy of this book with me. I hope to have it on top of my coffin. For all the world like the bishops have their hats and the soldiers have their swords and caps. Then when your man produces his edition of my deeds, I can produce my memoirs and we can compare notes. If the books do not tally, well, I do not know what I will do.

This particular edition could be read out at a religious knowledge period in any school. I am leaving this world with a very clean slate. I always knew I would die some day. Up to a few weeks ago, I was not sure when. With my lump on my back it is like being tied to a time-bomb that no-one has told you exactly the minute it will go off. Maybe my mentioning pain, agony and fear here and there along the pages has been tedious for some people. It is not half as tedious as it is for me, believe me.

As I look back over the years, I seem to have done very little. I have achieved nothing really. I have lived and I have loved. Given more time I could do both a lot better, I suppose.

I have no big black sin staining my lily white soul. I am not boasting when I say this. I am bloody well raging. I seemed to be always too busy or something to commit sin. Maybe I passed up loads of opportunities . I never noticed them, honest to God.

Now it is no use being given loads of opportunities. It is too late. To commit sin now would be like tearing up your train ticket and the train ready to start. For me the road ahead is straight, narrow and fierce short.

How have the years passed so quickly? Is it not like yesterday I was running barefoot around my grandmother's little town, the bells of the fuschia bobbing in the hedges as I ran wild with the dogs. I never listened to hear did those bells play a tune. I had not time. A week ago I took a day off from this book of mine and I again went back to that town. My grandmother's huge house was really only a normal sized one. The seaside with miles and miles of shingle was only a tiny little beach. The walk along the little town tired me out more than I like to admit. I sat in the seat near the church. It is the seat all the old men of the town sit in to catch their breath half-way up the hill to the paper shop. Running footsteps of a group of young children seemed to be my childhood clattering in my ears. A fuschia bush echoed my saddening thoughts with its bells in the spring breeze—it seemed to play the little song:

> Oh, the voice of the Kerry dances,
> Oh, the voice of the piper's tune,
> Oh, those wonderful hours of gladness,
> Gone alas, like our youth, too soon.

I left that town with a heavy heart. I shall never return to it as a child again. Probably I shall never return to it as an adult either. It is very sad that we have to pass on without being given a choice. I think anyway.

Back in my home town I have searched around the streets—where have all the years gone? Was I really young for all those years? Why should they pass so fast? What was I doing that I did not feel time passing? Oh, God, what was I doing? Am I the only person searching for their youth? I am not old yet. I am not fully used yet. Why do I have to go? I cannot turn the clock back. I cannot stop it and I certainly cannot slow down time. They say one has to hit the bottom of the pit of depression before one can come up once again. How many times have I hit the bottom? Millions. Now there does not seem to be any bottom. In this situation one cannot scream; it would do no good. One can not go into a corner; there is no corner really. What does one do when one's nerves are stretched like old elastic? Can I gather my dignity and go on with my story? Can I get myself out of this pit and get the story going in an amusing fashion. One is told that no one wants to read a depressing story. People want only to be amused. Oh, Jesus, help me.

Right. I have recovered sufficiently to rattle on. As well as putting a magnificent home around us, my husband and I have reared a beautiful little family. Those two things together are very time consuming in themselves. I am not giving you other people's opinions of our home and family — just ours!

We spent years at various hobbies. Hobbies are a way of passing time pleasantly and not being paid for same. We spent many happy hours in the toilet — developing our photographs. Every moment of every day is practically in black and white. The world can watch us growing up together with our son and daughter. Highlight after highlight, even the non-highlights, are there, plain for all to see.

Classical music became another hobby of ours. I never knew much about music. It was just a lovely sound which floated along and if I really liked it I floated along with it. We bought our first record player early on in our life together. My husband could sit for hours and dream and let the music float over him. I had jobs to do — what with the house, gardens and children. Then in the evenings, I, too, would down tools and listen to the music. Eventually I fell under it's spell too. Now I am an expert on Mozart and the rest of the boys. I love music, any type of music, but I have acquired a taste for the classical stuff during these past years. My favourite piece of music is *The Trout* by Schubert. If you have never heard it you have not lived. I think it depicts life in a very wonderful way. What he meant by it I do not know. While I sit and listen to this haunting music I can see the trout swimming against the tide. Then swimming with the tide and being swept along real happy-go-lucky like. It is a piece of music I would pick if I were being cremated.

A friend of my mother's was cremated in England.

Seemingly the coffin appeared when red velvet curtains were swished open. Music was played to amuse the mourners. Then as the red velvet curtains were swished closed again for the coffin to be removed the woman's favourite piece of music was played. Now that kind of thing would suit me no end. I would have *The Trout* as the curtains opened. I would have *The Trout* as the coffin — mine — laid on the stage and as the curtains would close for the last time — (you have guessed it) — *The Trout*'s music would continue on its happy way. I suppose it would be a bit much for the mourners. Still, it is what I would like. The only bit of music one would hear at our earthy funerals is the Last Post and one would have to be a soldier to have that. Music is out for me so, I suppose.

When we got a bit more opulent, we invested in stereo. A speaker was slung at each side of the dining room and the first stereo record was put on. Merciful God — I nearly died. I suppose it is the price one pays for not being blase. When I heard the women singing out of one speaker and the men out of the other, well I nearly died the death. Then the orchestra swept out through the fireplace and across the fire surround until I thought the flutes and things spits would be emptied out onto my good carpet. It was indeed a traumatic experience to feel they were in the room with us. I do not think I should ever get used to music. It is supposed to soothe the savage breast — isn't it? I would say it does all right. I could have put down a terrible day of pain and breaking things. God, I am a terror for breaking ware. A rent on it I am. Anyway, I would eventually have all the dirt of the day put away. The shoes cleaned for the morning. The uniforms out and ready. Hair ribbons ironed for school. Down I would sit and let the music float over me. There is no pleasure to equal it in this world.

But of course — we have another hobby. Anything — just anything seems great with this hobby. We have become experts on making homemade beer. Home Brew. Now we do not drink much as a rule. If we were to be given a few more years at this we would be turned into alcoholics, no bother.

We were for ages saying we would try it. We examined the cans of goo in the supermarkets. Would we? We would one day — then we would put it off. I went off to town one day and purchased a huge yellow plastic dustbin and a can of the stuff. We needed twenty bottles. Lucozade ones with the rubber tops. Easier said than done as they use screw tops now.

I went around and explained our predicament to various shopkeepers and we eventually got the right topped bottles. Following the directions on the tin of stuff we were off at a run. When the stuff was mature — its maturity was reached in the heat of our hot press — we bottled it. After our first glass of it we were finished. No bought beer ever tasted like it. It was super, divine, fabulous and fierce alcoholic altogether. After two glasses of it one can watch colour television on a black and white set. One can float up to bed and feel on top of the world. Maybe it is bad for us — who cares? Music has hidden meaning - more so under the influence of this stuff.

Very seldom now we go to our local. No more have we to suffer smoke from cigarettes grating our eye balls. No longer do we have to suffer people telling us stories we do not wish to hear. Most of which they have told us before anyway. No longer do they have to suffer us either. I have a fierce habit of trotting out the same stories again and again too. We can now sit with our flowing pints, at home, and listen to our own records. If anyone was there they would interrupt our listening. We are beginning to be very selfish in our twilight years. I am afraid! We can comment ourselves or stay silent. The music can soak into our very fibres. Maybe we do not get the exact message the composers tried to put over. But, just to sit and think that a human, a mere human, just like us, has made such music possible is enough to fill one with great humility. Music to me is the meaning of the word re-creation. After a record session I feel as if I have been remade — not any better, but at least, a lot happier. Gone are the worries and frustrations and I am ready to face the world again. Maybe not smiling, but at least not spitting with temper!

Another thing I find very relaxing is reading poetry. Love poems really used switch me on before. God have pity on me, I had not an ounce of sense. I suppose I never shall—but what matter?

Now I rather favour poems about flowers. As I do the gardens, I often mutter little snippets to myself. If the slugs have had a midnight feast I usually mutter curses. One poem I am crazy about - (have been for years) is a little one by Robert Herrick. I think it really matches my mood these days. Seeing as the next batch of daffodils will be the last I will see, I happen to be very attached to this. I recite it when I am feeling very sorry for myself and the tears flow down my face. Then I scold myself soundly and say, 'Jesus, will you get on with it.' I realise I am not dead yet, and there are a lot of dinners and the like to be done between this and—well.... here's the poem:—

TO DAFFODILS

'Fair Daffodils we weep to see
You haste away so soon;
As yet the early-rising sun
Has not attain'd his noon
Stay, Stay,
Until the hasting day
Has run
But to the evensong.
And, having pray'd together, we
Will go with you along.'

That is the first verse. Is it not really beautiful? I could imagine Robert and he sitting in a spring garden and feeling thoroughly depressed. I wonder if he had half a notion of going off with the dying daffodils? The length of his, and everyone's life, seemed to be really getting him down. If he was in the same boat as I, I daresay he would really loose his cool! I shall not spare you the drama of this poem so here is the second stanza:-

'We have short time to stay, as you,
We have as short a spring.
As quick a growth to meet decay,
As you, or anything.'

> *'We die,*
> *As your hours do, and dry*
> *Away.*
> *Like to the summer's rain;*
> *Or as the pearls of morning's dew,*
> *Ne'er to be found again.'*

For years that poem has appealed to me. As I look out of my windows and see the last of this spring's daffo - dils I feel a funny, lonely feeling coming over me. Birds sing and make nests—another year starts. The cycle of life continues.

I have grown from a daughter to a wife, then a mother. When will I grow into a cabbage? Each year something crops up and I am off on another project. Take this book. Oh, God, take it and welcome. Would a cabb- age be sitting here battering this misfortunate typewriter to death. A lunatic maybe, a cabbage—never! This bloody typewriter is driving me around the bend. It was going like a bomb until I decided to write my memoirs. Some devil has got into it. Twice already it has been to the local typewriter mender's place. It is going to drive me insane. This book is the last project I shall attempt and I shall die, if necessary, in the attempt. Remember Chopin in the film *A Song to Remember*? He died smashing—spitting blood on the piano—for a start. Then he declined away, pale but interesting, in a big bed. Me, I shall be strangled with a typewriter ribbon. I shall be the inkiest corpse ever seen!

I started off, as I told you, armed to the teeth with biros and copies. Those days are over. I got writer's cramp after one week. Page after page is filled into this monster and emptied out the other end typed. I would have loved to have had a ghost writer for this job. I could have filled him in on the highlights of my life. I could imagine myself sipping vodka—on ice, naturally—lounging on my sofa in a floral crafton or the like and giving him tit-bits of my exquisite life. Just imagine the expression on his face and he waiting for the juicy bits!

Instead of this I am here covered with ink. God never listened to me when I begged him to keep the grass down while I wrote this dream of a book.   No heed He took, no heed at all.   I have never seen such growth in my whole life.   The house had to be kept running on oiled wheels.   Meals produced in the same magical way as has been got used to by my family.   My social life, my private life, my public life and my love life have all to be kept going too.

I have never had such respect and admiration for authors before.   When I see our shelves of books —wow! We have only a small amount in comparison to the millions of millions trotted out each day of each year — all over the world. I have carted this bitch of a typewriter all over the house.   Anything for a change of outlook and scene.   How the hell do these other people do it?

Some of them go off by themselves for peace and quiet.   I suppose there is a lot to be said for it.   Others during interviews, say they can toss off books in the bosom of their families;   I do not know — there must be something wrong with the bosom of my family,   or with me.   Still seeing as I have got this far, it is not worth my while stopping now.

Heat (central now), comfort, good food, lovely clothes —all the material things of life.   The accumulation of the years really.   When we started first on the resounding bare boards, little did I think we would finish up with such comfort.   The change has been gradual from lino to carpets, from hand sewn curtains to machine stitched ones. Maybe some people take all these things for granted.   Maybe they started off with these things.   I do not consider them lucky.   I think we have been lucky.   We have got all our things slowly and surely.   We have been able to work for and savour each addition to our home and our lives as they came along.   Each year has brought its own particular blessings.   Each year we have grown wiser and more united.   We got more sense over the years and now can appreciate what we have.   More so than if we started with everything and took everything for granted.   All my dreams have come true.   Yet, one never stops dreaming, does one?   What would I like now?   What more could I ask for?   Pardon the drama but, Jesus,   I would like to die an old lady!

During one of our Saturday excursions to town we spotted vegetable seeds. We had never grown vegetables before on any big scale. Would we have a go?

We did set potatoes in our first year out at the house. One of my uncles by marriage came out in the back garden. He had one look at the potato plots and very respectfully took off his hat. He knelt at the side of the spud beds and blessed himself. He maintained it looked like the graves of Irish heroes of bygone days!

We did cabbage another year. Large, monstrous heads of green leather we grew. We ate it until it came out our eyes and so did most of our relations. One packet of seeds and we seemed to have about a thousand heads. Neighbours had gorgeous heads of green, beautiful cabbage and had a continuous battle with slugs to keep their stock intact. Not a slug went near our stuff. Bloody dynamite it was. Great as a laxative too it was. Still, we were only beginning. Onions we grew too in our youth. Strings upon strings of them slung around out of the garage roof, bobbing off my head every time I went out the kitchen door. Onions are supposed to prevent heart attacks. Having eaten our way through that particular crop, none of us will ever be in danger of a coronary anyway.

We got a packet of mixed seeds. Tomatoes, beet, lettuce, and onions. We nonchalantly put them in plastic containers filled with earth on the kitchen window sill. Jesus — we now have crops upon crops of the above mentioned. Our lawn is now disappearing as we have to thin out these numerous little seedlings. I think the one in charge of packing the seeds into our particular packet must have had a period. Her brains were not functioning anyway. There were millions of seeds in each packet and they have all come up. We shall be eating salads this summer and well into the autumn and winter by the look of things. Now instead of becoming a cabbage, I have to go out and fight the elements and the slugs off our crops. My husband suggested a scarecrow to be erected in the midst of his vegetables. I ask you? The neighbours have being growing vegetables on and off as the humour takes them, over the years. Never have I seen a scarecrow in their places. However, tomorrow I shall stuff some clothes and make one.

Then this summer we are off to another summer holiday. Destination, at the moment, not decided on. Then the schools will again open. Christmas will be in on top of us with the usual rushing and bustling. The spring will come again. The daffodils will bloom again.

Sometimes, when I get a moment to myself, I stand at my windows and look out. The seasons will chase each other across the gardens. Often these days I get very tired and stand for a few seconds. The lace curtains hide me from my passing neighbours. They pass laughing and talking as they go to the shop. Sometimes I join them on my way for the bit of dinner. My laugh is as gay as theirs and my voice is as cheerful. Then when I again get inside my lace curtain—my heart breaks. The little babies they wheel in their prams, I shall never see them going to school. These friends of mine will probably get a big shock when they see the crepe on our gate. It is an awful sensation to see a crepe on a neighbour's door. As I look out at them I think these morbid thoughts.

What can I do? One cannot scream or shout out of one's window. What is there to shout. 'I am dying — help me!'

They can do nothing. They are even more helpless than the doctors. As I wave the children off to school, I feel terrible. My children—who will wave them off next year? Who will kiss them good-night? There is my hus-band—what am I going to do about him? How am I going to tell him next spring. Will I last until then? Would I have been better not to have ever loved him? Is it my fault now that four of us are caught in a web? We are caught in a web of love and I wove it. God—where do I turn now?

I jokingly thought of suicide before as making a great impression appearing floating along Galway Bay. God give me sense. I have courted the idea recently again. Just to put an end to all the pain and misery which I know is going to come. But I could not do it. I have not the nerve.

Anyway I do not think suicide is a dignified way to die. I may not have lived with dignity. You see I have dashed into one thing after another. I have run where others have walked. I seem to always be in a hurry. Maybe in my innermost heart I have foreseen that I was not going to be given much time really. The fist of years I've had was not terribly generous really. Forgive me, Jesus, but that is the truth!

Anyway, even if I have not lived with dignity, I am determined to die with dignity. I do not want my family to have a finger pointed at them and the word whispered that I had 'done myself in', so to speak. No I will stick it out to the bitter end no matter what happens.

While I examine my life, I can see no great deeds that I have done. I seemed to have done damn all really. It must be wonderful to face death with a feeling that one has been useful in some way. To have invented something: at times I have thought I have invented love — appreciation of nature and music and everything. I imagine no one else can feel about things as I feel about them. In that I know I am a fool. But, I try telling myself that and I do not wish to listen. No one, I reply to myself, can feel like I feel and that is that!

What will become of my mother — who will keep an eye on her? I am not going to warn her I am going to leave her. She who fought death for me all those years ago. It was she who put me and kept me on the straight and narrow road. She praised me when I succeeded and consoled me when I failed. How can I turn around now and break her heart? No one should ask me to do that. Who will tell my children? What am I going to do?

As the pages of this book go speeding by so also my life goes speeding by. Neither can be stopped. The book is ending now in a very few lines. My life is also finished. I have never felt so utterly helpless. Trying to hold onto life now seems to me like trying to get a hold on a crumbling cliff. Am I being selfish thinking of myself all the time. God, I think I am, but I really cannot help it. What about my loved ones? Who will console them? Will all the tears I shed now do any good? Not likely to -